D0113844

THE VENGEANCE OF
THE GODS

REX WARNER

THE

VENGEANCE
OF
THE GODS

ILLUSTRATED BY
SUSAN EINZIG

[East Lansing]

MICHIGAN
STATE COLLEGE PRESS

1955

FIRST PUBLISHED 1955
IN U.S.A.

BL781
.W3
Copy 2

Ainsley
10-2-62
049

PRINTED IN GREAT BRITAIN BY
ROBERT CUNNINGHAM AND SONS LTD., ALVA

FOREWORD

NEARLY all these stories have been taken from the plays of Euripides, though for Prometheus and for Agamemnon I have followed Aeschylus and some other sources.

R.W.

CONTENTS

ILLUSTRATIONS

PROMETHEUS

PROMETHEUS

ACCORDING to the old stories the gods themselves, like men, have changed and altered. Just as men were once wild and savage, and just as they struggled amongst themselves, and still struggle, for power and supremacy, so, at the very beginning of things there was warfare and enmity and deceit among the gods. Even Zeus did not establish himself without difficulty; nor was he always perfectly wise and good. Not everyone believes these early stories, and there are some who say that it is wrong to tell such stories at all; for how can we believe that the gods ever did things which men themselves would be ashamed to do? However the stories are still told. One of them concerns the anger of Zeus with the good Titan, Prometheus, the friend and benefactor of mankind. But to understand this story it is necessary first to go back to the very beginning of all things.

First of all, they say, was Chaos, a wide-open yawning space, something in which it was impossible for any thing to be separated from or combined with any other thing; for indeed there were no things at all. But from Chaos there came Gaia, the Earth, the Mother of all things. And

Gaia created from herself Ouranos, the great vault of the starry Heaven, to enfold her and to be her equal and her mate. Many children were born to Gaia and to Ouranos. First was the whole race of the Titans, – father Oceanus, whose salt streams encircle the world, great Iapetus, who was the father of Prometheus, and many others, youngest of whom and most cunning was Cronos. And apart from these Gaia bore a monstrous brood, the huge Cyclopes, who had one eye in the middle of their foreheads, and great creatures of enormous strength, the giants, each of whom had fifty heads and a hundred arms.

As for Ouranos, from the very first he hated all his children. As soon as they were born, he hid them away in the depths of the earth and would not allow any one of them to see the light. So they were restrained as it were in the very body of their mother and both they and their mother were angry. Then Gaia herself thought out a cruel plan. Out of her own body she formed a hard metal, either iron or flint, and from this she made a sharp sickle. Then she spoke to her sons and asked them to avenge her on Ouranos, so as to cut him off entirely from her, since it was he first who had done such shameful deeds and had imprisoned them from the light of day. But the sons all feared their father, all except Cronos who said to Gaia, 'Mother, I will undertake to do this thing, since I care nothing for our father, whose name I hate; and it was he first who did wrong.'

So Cronos took the sickle and when at night Ouranos came down from Heaven, to lie with his bride the Earth, he waited for him in ambush and with this sickle he cut off from him his male parts and hurled them from him into the sea. Now from the wound the drops of blood which fell upon the earth were fertile and out of them sprang the terrible goddesses, the Erinyes who pursue with vengeance all those who are guilty of shedding a father's or a mother's blood; and from the sea into which fell the outraged members of Ouranos there arose, from the very foam of the sea, a great goddess, lovely and powerful, the laughter-loving Aphrodite, who has her hold over the hearts of gods and men. Out of the sea sprang her immortal body and she came first to the island of Cythera and from there to Cyprus, and around her white feet the grass grew green and sweet flowers opened in their blossoms. Desire and Longing went with her, and she took at once her great place amongst the powers that be.

As for Ouranos, he withdrew to the Heaven which he had named. His sons, he said, had done a dreadful deed and this would not go unpunished.

And now Cronos became King among the gods; but it had been revealed to him by his mother, Gaia, that he was destined to lose his sovereignty and to be overthrown by one of his own sons. Cronos did his best, but unavailingly, to guard against this event. His wife was the Titaness Rhea and she bore to him great children, the goddesses Hestia, Demeter and Hera and the gods

Hades, Poseidon and Zeus. Cronos, fearing the future, had no wish for any of his children to exist and, as soon as they were born, while they were still in swaddling clothes, he took them from their mother and swallowed them. This cruelty was something which their mother, Rhea, could not bear, and when the time came for her to give birth to Zeus, her youngest child, she determined to outwit her husband. And so, instead of giving Cronos the child, she gave him a large stone wrapped round in swaddling clothes and it was this stone which Cronos swallowed, thinking that it was his own son. Meanwhile Zeus was being secretly brought up in the island of Crete. Gaia herself took charge of him and instructed him in the arts of seizing power. So, after time had passed and Zeus had grown to his full strength, he fell upon his father Cronos and bound him with chains, overcoming him by superior force and by superior cunning. He forced him to disgorge from his belly all those children whom he had previously swallowed down, and first out came the stone which Cronos had believed to be Zeus himself. This stone was set down in Delphi and in later times was reverently anointed by the Delphians with oil.

And now, in place of Cronos, Zeus, with his great brothers and sisters, ruled. Not only did Zeus free the children of Cronos and Rhea, but also those monstrous creatures, children of Gaia and Ouranos, whom Ouranos had imprisoned in the deep places of the earth. And these sons of

Heaven were grateful to him and gave him the lightning and thunder, weapons by which he could confirm his supremacy.

Still, however, there were quarrels among the gods and among the children of the gods, and still the house of Zeus was not so firmly established that it was unshakeable. There were still among the old Titans those who preferred the rule of Cronos to that of Zeus; there were still the great giants and earth-born creatures who, in their immense strength, believed that brute force could never be resisted and that sheer weight and size were more important than skill, intelligence and cunning. So, against Titans and giants, Zeus and the newer gods had to fight in order to preserve their power and authority. And in these fights it is said that Zeus was greatly helped by the advice of the Titan Prometheus, the cleverest of all his race, to whom his mother Gaia had revealed the truth that in the future victory would not go to ignorant force or to might but to those who were able to think and to plan ahead.

And so in the end the empire of Zeus was firmly established. The dreadful monsters who had refused to submit to him were either destroyed by his thunderbolts or bound and fettered underground. The other gods had their appointed places and, though they might quarrel amongst themselves, none of them would venture to oppose the will of Zeus. But Zeus, as is the way with those who have newly risen to power, was still jealous of others, still determined to insist upon

B

his authority. In particular he was most grudging in his gifts to men and it was here that he came into conflict with the wise Titan Prometheus who had helped him to gain his position of absolute supremacy.

There are many different stories told as to how men themselves came into being. Some say that they appeared lying on the ground under the ash trees and so were, in some sense, the children of the nymphs who are the guardian spirits of those trees. According to others they were formed inside the earth by the gods out of earth and fire and all the elements that can be mixed with them. It is said too that they were actually created by Prometheus himself. However this may be, it is agreed that in the beginning man was a weak, ignorant and defenceless creature.

But Prometheus, for some reason of his own, loved this weak and pitiful race. He saw them living like animals in caves, adapting themselves as best they could to each day that came, and he it was who taught them how to distinguish the seasons, one from another, how to follow the risings and the settings of the stars, the beginning of civilisation. He taught them how to use numbers and how to form letters to serve as signs for the sounds they made in speech and so finally to become the means by which knowledge could be recorded and the beauty and strength of thought and feeling be made to last for ever. He told them the way to tame wild animals, cattle and horses and dogs, so that they might relieve man's burden

PROMETHEUS LOVED THIS WEAK RACE

and help him in his work. He showed the sailors how to build boats that could float upon the waters and be carried forward on wings of sails. He taught them the meaning of the behaviour of birds and of their flight, so that by observing them they might know the future. In a word, it was Prometheus who gave men every art and every science; and finally he gave them the gift of fire. According to one story Prometheus stole the fire from the island of Lemnos where stood the forge and workshop of Hephaestus, the master crafts-man among the gods; according to other stories he took the fire from the very hearth of Zeus himself on Olympus and brought it to man concealed in the hollow stem of a plant.

Now Zeus was a jealous god. He grudged men all the gifts that Prometheus had given them and he was angry with Prometheus for granting to these wretched creatures of an hour the ability to shape their lives into something better and to raise their thoughts up to the heaven itself. And so when he found that Prometheus had given to man this final gift of fire, he burst out into un-controllable rage. He ordered his two invincible servants, Power and Violence, to seize Prome-theus and to carry him to the highest peak of the dreadful Caucasus. There among the crawling glaciers, beneath the lashing hail and winds of storm, or, in the summer time, shelterless against the scorching heat of the sun, Prometheus was to be bound fast with unbreakable chains. The task of making these massive chains and of fastening

them upon the victim's body was given to Hephaestus, and, though Hephaestus shrank from the
dreadful deed of so torturing a brother god, he
feared the power of Zeus and did not dare to
disobey. Indeed he hated the skill of his hand,
but he was forced to use it, and so he flung the
hard chains around the immortal body of Prometheus and, with great blows of his hammer, nailed
and fastened him to the towering rocks. He
groaned as he did this work, for he pitied the good
Titan; but the servants of Zeus, Power and Violence, merely mocked him for his weak spirit and
hurled their insults at Prometheus himself. 'You
did good to men', they said, 'against the will of
Zeus. Now see if there is any help to be found in
men.' And they taunted him with his name,
which means 'Forethought'. 'You will need more
forethought than you have,' they said, 'if you are
ever to break out again into freedom from these
eternal chains.'

But neither to them nor to Hephaestus did
Prometheus speak a word, and so they left him
nailed against the mountain side, a god tortured
at the hands of gods. And as for Prometheus,
though his body was chained to the rocks, his
mind remained stubborn and unconquered. Zeus
had the power to control his body in unbreakable
fetters, but not Zeus himself could alter or subdue
his fixed and steady mind and persuade him that
there was anything in this punishment but black
ingratitude and base injustice. Zeus owed the
very power he wielded to the help given him by

Prometheus; nor had Prometheus ever rebelled against the power of Zeus; his only crime had been to help mortal men to escape from savagery and to raise themselves, by knowledge, higher than the beasts.

Now there were many of the gods who pitied Prometheus and among these was the Titan, Father Oceanus, who surrounds the world with his life-giving stream. He left the self-made caves of rock in which he lived and came up to earth to give Prometheus the best advice he could, urging him to make his submission to Zeus. 'For Zeus,' he said, 'has absolute power, and it is useless to fight against it. Whether you are right or wrong, it will make no difference. Surely it is better to relax your anger and to speak humbly to one who is more powerful than you are. And, if only you will do this, I myself will go to Zeus and will beg him to forgive you and the other gods will join me in their prayers.'

But Prometheus would have none of this intervention, which seemed to him both disgraceful and useless. Zeus, he considered, was behaving like some dictator, whose lust for power was forcing him beyond the limits. Zeus had already destroyed many of the older gods and for these now Prometheus began to feel pity. There was his own brother, Atlas, who, by the will of Zeus, stood in the regions of the west and carried on his vast shoulders the whole weight of the heavens, a difficult burden which he could never shake off. And there was the great hundred-headed monster

Typhon, the child of Heaven and Earth, who had been blasted to ruin by the thunderbolt of Zeus and now lay, a useless frame, beneath the roots of Etna, though still his anger boiled and the hot heaving of his breath would, from time to time, force fire and molten rock into the air and devastate all the fields of smiling Sicily. And so Prometheus told Oceanus to beware lest, if he took the side of one of the older gods, some such a fate as this might fall upon him too. As for himself, he said, no power and no pain would ever make him bow the knee to the tyrant of the gods. For century after century Zeus might hurl fresh pain upon him but would never conquer his unyielding spirit. Nor was Zeus himself secure for ever in his power. For, just as Ouranos had given way to Cronos and Cronos himself had been overmastered by Zeus, so, said Prometheus, there was a moment fixed in the hidden and distant future when Zeus, if he made a certain marriage, would become the father of a son mightier than himself, one who would laugh at lightning and thunderbolts, since he would possess a weapon far greater than these, and who, with a motion of the hand would brush aside the great trident of Poseidon, the earth-shaker. Prometheus who was wise with the wisdom of his mother Earth, knew the secret of this wedding and who it was, if ever she became the bride of Zeus, that was destined to bear a child more powerful than the present supreme ruler of gods and men. But, said Prometheus, he would never reveal this secret – never, until he was released from these chains and restored to the honours he had before. Nor could any exercise of supreme power make him in any manner of way alter his mind.

So Oceanus returned to the deep sea caves where he lives remote from the quarrels of gods in heaven and of men on earth. He might have wished that Prometheus could have been less unbending in his spirit, but he feared for himself if he were to do more in the matter.

But Zeus, who hears everything, had heard the words spoken by Prometheus and knew that in the possession of this chained and helpless captive was a secret which, if it were not told, might at some time or other, near or far, mean the end of his own power and an ignominious fall. He could not bear to think that anyone could hold, or could be allowed to remain holding, an advantage over him, and so he sent down from Olympus his messenger, the god Hermes, to that crag in the Caucasus where Prometheus stood chained. Hermes came and delivered his message, which was that Prometheus must tell at once that secret of which he had been boasting; if he did not, punishment far more fearful than any he had yet known would come down upon him.

But Prometheus treated both the message and the messenger with contempt. 'I hate and despise', he said, 'your master Zeus, and I would rather be the slave for ever to this bitter barren rock than his trusted servant. I know the power of Zeus and, though I may feel it, I do not fear it.

Let him let loose upon me all the fires of his lightning, all the blows of thunder from above and
beneath the earth. Let him mix earth and heaven
together over my head. Never, till I am released
from these bonds, shall I reveal to him the thing
he wishes to know and the thing which will, in
the end, plunge him downward from his dic-
tatorship.'

Nor did any words that Hermes could speak
have any effect upon the Titan's unbending pride.
'Try', Hermes begged him, 'to make your thought
follow the meaning of your position. Be humble,
since there is no help. For, if you persist in refusing to speak, Father Zeus will convulse this
whole mountain with thunder and lightning.
You will be buried in the depths of the earth and
you will groan as the weight of the earth bears
down upon you. And then, shattered and broken,
you will be brought up to the light of day; and
now, every day, the winged hound of Zeus, his
great eagle, will fly to you and every day will tear
the flesh of your body into rags, feasting upon
your liver and gnawing it black; and every night
the flesh will grow again to be destroyed and torn
to fragments as the next day comes. There will
be no end ever to these fearful pains, nor am I
threatening anything that will not be done; for
Zeus will bring every word I have spoken to
actual fact.'

But no threat and no certain knowledge could
turn the mind of Prometheus. 'You have told
me', he said, 'nothing that I did not know already.

The hound of Zeus may tear my body into shreds; my frame may be broken and shattered beneath earthquakes and falling skies; my mind remains immortal and unsubdued.'

So Hermes departed hurriedly, lest he might find himself involved in that terrible convulsion of nature that he knew was now to fall upon the mountain where still Prometheus stood to challenge a superior power. And soon indeed came the crashing and reverberation of thunder, the the roar and howling of winds, the quaking of the earth and the loose-flung torches and solid sheets of burning and corroding lightning. Yet in this shattering storm and conflagration of nature Prometheus, flung from wave to wave of terror, pierced by the jagged rocks and overloaded by the pressing weight of mountain ranges, never altered for one moment the fixed resolution of a mind determined to resist. Nor, later, when his mangled body was restored to the upper air, did he weaken beneath the pain as every day the eagle of Zeus came to feed upon his flesh. Every night the flesh was renewed and every day there was reiterated pain. Yet still Prometheus kept his secret and still, in the face of unending persecution, defied the supreme power.

How could this story end except in the fulfilment of the threat which Prometheus had made, or else in some alteration in the character of either Zeus or Prometheus or both? It seems that it was this latter thing that happened. It seems, though this is a hard thing to say of gods, that

Zeus, as he grew older in power, grew wiser and more merciful; and it may be too that Prometheus himself, though he lost nothing of his resolution, may have relaxed something of his pride. What is certain is that some form of persuasion was found to intervene between these mighty antagonists. Prometheus was freed and freed by the son of Zeus, Hercules, who climbed the high Caucasus and, after shooting down the eagle with his arrows, released the great Titan from his chains. And Prometheus revealed the secret which he had kept so long and through such sufferings. It was that if Zeus, as he was minded to do, were to marry the sea-goddess, silver-footed Thetis, then she would bear a son stronger than the father. And so Zeus and the other blessed gods betrothed Thetis to a mortal, fearing the event if she were to marry one of them. They chose for her husband the great king of Thessaly, Peleus, and by him, as is well known, she became the mother of the greatest warrior of all men who lived upon the earth, though he died very young, the fleet-footed Achilles.

As for Zeus and for Prometheus, their quarrel was over. Each had, in a manner, submitted to the other, and, though differences still arose among the blessed gods, never again was there to be any struggle in heaven for supreme power.

ION

ION

WHERE the walls of the citadel of Athens look northwards there is a steep rocky place that is called 'the Long Cliffs', and in these cliffs there is a cave. Here, in very ancient times, the god Apollo committed a crime against a mortal woman. The woman, or rather the young girl, was Creusa, daughter of King Erechtheus of Athens. Apollo, with the overpowering strength of a god, surprised her and forced her, in spite of her tears and her unwillingness, to become his mate. So, ravished by the god, she conceived a child and, when the time came for her to give birth, she gave birth secretly so that only one or two of her most trusted servants knew of it. Then, since she was ashamed to have a child and not a husband, she wrapped the baby in swaddling clothes and put him in a cradle made, like a basket, of woven willow twigs. She set by his head golden ornaments in the shape of snakes, – such ornaments as were always worn in those days by members of the royal family of Athens, – and she carried the baby to that very cave in the Long Cliffs where she had been surprised and outraged by Apollo. Here, though with a sad heart, she left the child, not knowing

31

whether he would be found and taken care of by some shepherd or traveller or whether he might become the prey of the wild beasts and the birds. But later she repented of what she had done and went back to the cave. She found it empty. There was no sign either of the baby or of the cradle in which she had laid him. So she went away unhappy and gave him up for lost.

Yet the child had not been devoured by wild beasts nor had he fallen into the hands of strangers. Apollo himself had taken him up in his cradle, just as he lay, and carried him to his own great sanctuary and temple at Delphi. He had set the cradle down inside the court of the temple and he had put it into the heart of the Pythia, his chief prophetess and the one who in her own voice declared his oracles, to find the baby and to bring him up as a servant of the god. So Ion (for this was the name given to the child of Creusa and Apollo) grew up in the temple to be a strong and beautiful young man and delighted in serving the great god who was, though he did not know it, his own father. The tasks which he had to do were tasks which gave him pleasure, for he worshipped Apollo in purity of heart and thought of him as the source of all truth, all splendour and all perfection.

So, with the first light of every day, Ion would rise and see that everything in the temple was in order. He would sprinkle over the floors the holy water taken from the springs of Castalia and with branches of the bay tree he would sweep and

clean the whole building. Then, with his bow
and arrows in his hand, he would sit in the bright
sunlight and would chase away any birds that
might come to defile the temple's golden roof or
to snatch up some portion of the sacrifices. For
from the high cliffs of Mount Parnassus which
rise like a great wall to the sky behind the holy
place the jackdaws and ravens would come
circling out with their harsh cries and, wheeling
above them, would be the eagles and the vultures;
while, from the river valley below and the silver-
green of innumerable olive trees, sometimes the
white swans would come flying with outstretched
necks towards the gorgeous habitation of the god.
All these birds Ion would scare away with his
arrows, keeping the temple pure and delighting
in the care that he took to do so. He knew nothing
of his own parents and, though he sometimes
wondered who they could be, he was proud to
be known as 'the servant of Apollo' and content
with the life that he led.

Yet he had a more glorious fate in front of him
than he imagined, and he was to learn to know
his parents, though the knowledge would give
him pain and, in acquiring it, he was to run into
danger.

While Ion had been growing up at Delphi, his
mother Creusa continued to live in Athens. After
the death of her father, King Erechtheus, the
Athenians suffered much in war. From the
neighbouring island of Euboea great forces came
against them, ravaging the countryside and de-

c

feating the Athenians themselves in battle. In the end, however, the Athenians found a man who was both a skilful general and a stout warrior, and under his leadership they drove back their enemies and were able once more to enjoy the pleasures of peace and power. This man, whose name was Xuthus, was not an Athenian himself, but an Achaean; yet he served the Athenians so well that they gave him as a reward the hand of Creusa, the King's daughter, in marriage.

So for some time Xuthus and Creusa lived happily together. Only one thing disturbed their happiness and this was that they had no children. At length Xuthus determined to consult the oracle of Apollo at Delphi, and he set out on the road northward from Athens, taking his wife Creusa with him. Creusa herself was glad to go. Not that she loved the god Apollo, who had betrayed her; but she wanted to bear children to rule in Athens and also she hoped, or half-hoped, that the oracle might reveal to her what had been the fate of that one child whom she had born in the past, though she had little enough hope that he survived anywhere on the earth.

It was Creusa who arrived first at Apollo's shining temple of Delphi; she had come ahead of her husband since he had delayed on the way in order to consult another oracle, the oracle of Trophonius, whose ancient and sacred place is in a rocky gorge at the foot of the great mountain mass of Parnassus up which goes the road to

Apollo's sanctuary at Delphi. It was by this road
that Creusa travelled, with her women servants
and her armed attendants, and, when they came
in sight of Delphi itself they were amazed at the
statues of gold and marble and bronze that stood
there, at the shrines and altars set up by cities or
by great men, and most of all, at the sight of
Apollo's own temple with its golden roof and the
fine carvings in stone of the deeds of heroes and
of gods.

But when Creusa saw this temple, so gloriously
built to show the greatness of the god, what she
remembered was his violence against her and his
treachery, and the tears fell from her eyes as she
stood gazing at all this magnificence. And now
her tears were interrupted by the voice of a young
man, the attendant at the gates of the temple,
who was indeed her own son Ion, though she did
not know this, nor did he know that he was now
seeing his mother for the first time. He asked her
in surprise why she was weeping, since to him
the house of Apollo was a house of joy and peace.
Creusa said that she wept because of the misdeeds
done by the gods, but this was something which
Ion could not imagine or understand. 'All goodness comes from the gods,' he said. 'How can the
gods do evil?'

Then Creusa told him of the question which
she wished to ask Apollo's oracle. But, since she
did not wish her own story to be known, she disguised the facts. She said that she had a friend,
one of the women of Athens, who had borne a

child to the god Apollo and who had then been deserted by him. This friend of hers, said Creusa, did not even know whether her child was alive or dead, though she feared that he was dead. She wanted the oracle to tell her just this, – was the child still living or had he been devoured by the wild beasts?

Ion was shocked and horrified both by the question and by the story which lay behind it. He could not believe that the great god, whose servant he was and whom he worshipped in such purity of heart, could have done this injury to a mortal woman or allowed his own child to perish. 'This story of yours,' he said to Creusa, 'is not one in which I myself can possibly have any faith, even though it seems that your friend has succeeded in persuading you to believe in it. But I am sure that the gods do not do such things. And, even if there were any truth in the story, would not Apollo see to it that his son was safe and happy, perhaps in some place of his own far away from Athens? However, in any case the question which your friend wishes to ask cannot be asked here. Here we approach the god with reverence.'

Creusa saw that Ion would not help her to have her question put to the oracle of Apollo. While the young man had been speaking she had looked at him closely and had admired the beauty of his appearance and the grace and sincerity of his words. Her own son, she thought, if only he had lived would now be of the same age as this young man and might have had just such a noble look. She began to question him as to who his parents were and from what city he came. But when Ion told her his story – that he did not know his parents and that from childhood he had been brought up in the temple of Apollo – it still never entered her thoughts that here in front of her was the very child whom she imagined to be dead and hoped might, by some chance, be alive. Nor, of course, could Ion have guessed that this lady, the Queen of famous Athens, was his mother and that his father was the great god whom he worshipped.

And now, while they were still in conversation, Creusa's husband, the warrior King Xuthus arrived. He had visited the oracle of Trophonius and had then made haste to follow his wife, since he had good news to tell. The oracle had not given a full reply, since it was known that Xuthus was on his way to the prophetic place of Apollo. Only one sentence had been spoken and it was this: 'Neither you, Xuthus, nor your wife Creusa will return childless from Delphi.'

Xuthus had been greatly heartened by this sentence and, after he had greeted his wife and told her of his good hopes, he asked to be allowed to go at once into the inner sanctuary so that he might consult the oracle of the god. So Creusa, with her women, retired to her place of lodging to await the news that her husband would bring; and now she herself felt her heart lightened, for she, just as much as Xuthus, wished to have a child who would rule in Athens after her death.

As for Ion, he performed his task, which was to admit Xuthus into the inner sanctuary, and then he took up his usual position in front of the temple gates. But now his spirit was unusually restless, for he had been disturbed by the story which Creusa had told him. Was it possible, he wondered, that it might be true? And, if it were true, what was he to think of the gods? For, if the gods acted no better than sinful men, how could they deserve to be worshipped?

So he sat still in the high mountain air, uneasily thinking to himself, when he was surprised once more by an event which he could scarcely have imagined. For now the temple gates were opened and Xuthus, with every expression of joy upon his face, came out into the bright sunlight and, seeing Ion, hurried towards him with outstretched arms, as though eager to embrace him. Ion, at the sight of the great warrior advancing upon him with such curious signs of affection, started back a pace. His first thought was that Xuthus had somehow lost his wits, and he fitted an arrow to his bow, so that, if necessary, he would be able to defend himself. But Xuthus, still with a most joyful face, merely cried out to him: 'Shoot at me, if you will; but, if you do shoot, you will be shooting your own father.' At this Ion stood still in astonishment. Again he felt convinced that Xuthus must be out of his mind; but Xuthus hastened to explain that for what he said he had the authority of the god Apollo himself. He had asked the oracle whether he could have children and the oracle had replied that, not only would Apollo grant him children but that the first person he saw on leaving the temple would be his son. It was Ion whom he had seen first and it was Ion therefore who was his son.

Indeed it seemed impossible to doubt the words of the god, but still some mystery remained. 'Who then can be my mother?' Ion asked. But Xuthus was so delighted at having discovered a son, that he had not yet even given a thought to the subject of who the child's mother might be. And even now he was most uncertain, as indeed was natural, considering that Ion was not really his son at all. He could remember that in his youth, before he had married Creusa, he had once come to Delphi and had taken part in the nightly revels in honour of Bacchus, the god of wine. At these revels the worshippers are often drunk with wine and it sometimes happens that children are born afterwards without anyone having a very clear idea of how they came to be conceived. So now it seemed to Xuthus that perhaps some woman of Delphi, whose existence he had entirely forgotten, had been the mother of Ion and had secretly placed the child in the temple of Apollo, where he had remained ever since. To Ion also this appeared to be the most likely explanation and, although he was saddened by the thought that he would never know who his mother was, he was glad to think that he was not the son of a slave, since only free-born women were allowed to take part in the festivals of Bacchus, and he had at least discovered (or he thought he had discovered) a father who was a great warrior and the ruler of Athens.

As for Xuthus, he was so pleased with what had happened that he forgot a most important consideration which was that his wife, Creusa, had also been promised a child. He was so full of his own joy that he scarcely thought of what her feelings would be when she discovered that, while he had a child whom he would make King of Athens, she herself, an Athenian born of the royal house, was still childless. Ion was more quick than Xuthus to realise the difficulties that might lie ahead. He saw that not only might Creusa hate him for taking a place that ought properly to belong to her own children, but that also the Athenians themselves might not be willing to accept him, since neither his father nor mother was of Athenian blood. And so when Xuthus told him with glee of how he would make him rich and famous at Athens, Ion himself could not enter into the joy of his supposed father. Indeed he almost wished that this discovery had not been made and that he might continue to live humbly as he had done, in peace and quiet at Delphi, serving the god Apollo and innocent of the world outside the temple of the god. But Xuthus would hear nothing of these misgivings. What he wished to do at once was to hold a great feast at which he would publicly acknowledge his son and do him all the honour that a great and powerful king could do.

So he and Ion began immediately to make the preparations for a banquet. Huge tents and pavilions were pitched upon the level ground and were so arranged that neither the fierce rays of the sun at midday nor the slanting light of evening could disturb the feasters. Sheep and oxen were slaughtered and prepared for the tables; wine, fruit, eggs, olives and all good things were ordered in abundance and all the people of Delphi were invited to join in the festival.

Meanwhile Creusa had been waiting in her own lodging to hear what had been the reply of the oracle to her husband. At length a faithful servant of her's, an old man who had known her since her childhood, came to her with the news; but it was not at all the news that she had expected or desired. The servant also was indignant, for, though he loved King Xuthus, he loved his mistress more. It seemed to him unfair that, while Xuthus should have a son, Creusa should have been left unnoticed by the god. Moreover this son of Xuthus, Ion, was as it seemed, an alien, and yet he was to rule in Athens. And so the old man allowed the state of his own mind to influence him as he told the story and, although he did not tell Creusa anything that was untrue, he laid most weight on those things in it that would most displease her.

Creusa herself was made both angry and wretched by what she heard. She loved her husband, but she could not bear the thought of a stepson taking the place that should have belonged to a child of her own. And now too it seemed to her that she had been betrayed a second time by Apollo who had not only taken away his own child from her, but was giving to her husband another child, a stranger, while for her there was nothing left in life which could give her pleasure or hope. She now began to hate the young man Ion, whom, when she had seen him at first, she had so admired; and she was ready to listen to the old servant who suggested that she and all the people of Athens were being tricked. For might it not be, the old man said, that Xuthus had betrayed his wife and had become the father of a son by some slave girl; that he had had the child brought up at Delphi and had then, no doubt with the aid of some corrupt priest of the god, arranged beforehand that when he came to Delphi pretending to be interested in the birth of children to himself and his wife, this child should be declared openly to be his and to be the heir to the throne of Athens? In all this, so the old servant suggested, he had never even thought of his wife and now he was actually making merry in his own good fortune and in her misery.

Creusa, in her anger and her dismay, came to believe that this was in fact what had happened; and now her thoughts began to turn to revenge. Most of all she would have wished to revenge herself on Apollo himself and to have burned down his whole temple and sanctuary. She was angry too with her husband; but when the old servant suggested that she should take his life, she shrank back in horror from the idea; for even though she was angry with Xuthus, she still loved him and respected him. It seemed best to her to take, or attempt to take, the life of the young man, Ion; for, in so doing, she would both hurt her husband and free herself of the prospect and of the reality of having to live and see her husband happy in the presence of a son of his own, while she herself was childless. So she took this wicked resolution and proceeded to carry it into effect, little knowing that what she was planning to do was not only to kill an innocent man, but to kill her own and Apollo's child.

The old servant was willing enough to help her. He took from her some poison so deadly that a single drop of it would be sufficient to kill a man instantly. It would be easy for him to make use of it since he was to be in charge of serving the wine at the feast. So he went off confidently to carry out the treacherous plot, and Creusa waited equally confidently for the news of its success and of the cruel revenge which, she thought, would bring comfort to her vexed and tortured spirit.

By this time a herald had been through Delphi inviting all who wished to come to the feast. The tent was thronged with the guests who came and soon they were sitting down with garlands on their heads, eating and drinking to their hearts' content. After they had eaten their fill the old servant of Creusa saw to it that water was carried round so that they might wash their hands. Then Xuthus himself retired from the feast, for he wished to make in private the proper sacrifices to the gods that are made at the birth of a son. This to him seemed to be his own son's birthday and, as he went, he left Ion behind as master of the feast. And now the old servant ordered fresh wine to be brought out together with new and bigger cups of gold and silver. Into one of these cups he put the poison and then, filling it with wine, he gave it to Ion, pretending that he was honouring him as his new master. Ion raised the cup to his lips and all the other feasters prepared to drink with him and to wish him happiness. But, just as he was about to take this drink that would certainly have destroyed him, Ion happened to hear one of the servants making some remark which he, with his knowledge of prophecy, thought to be ill-omened. He therefore called out to the guests not to drink the wine in their cups, but to pour it out on the ground in honour to the gods and then to have their cups refilled. In silence they all did as he said and he himself first poured on to the ground the wine from his own cup. And now, by the will of the gods, the plot that had been made against his life was discovered. For there are many doves which live unmolested in the place sacred to Apollo and some of them had flown into the tent where the feast was being held. One dove, and one only, approached the drink offering that had been made to the gods and she came to that spot of ground where Ion had emptied out his cup. But no sooner had the dove dipped her beak in the spilt wine than she

ION AND THE POISONED DOVE

gave a strange cry and began to flap her wings and roll her neck in agony. Everyone wondered at the sight of the bird struggling in its pain; but the pain did not last long; suddenly the pink claws relaxed and the dove fell on her side dead.

And now Ion threw his cloak aside and leapt upon the old man who had given him the cup. 'It was you,' he shouted, 'who tried to murder me. Confess who it was who set you on to do it, or else you die immediately.'

As for the old servant, surrounded as he was by the angry guests and threatened with torture unless he spoke the truth, he was so terrified that he told everything. Creusa, it was now known, had not only plotted against Ion's life, but had so contrived her plot that, if it had been successful, the young man would have been killed on ground sacred to Apollo. The penalty for murder or attempted murder in the god's sanctuary was a clear one, and it was at once decreed by the rulers of Delphi that Creusa should be taken to the top of the high rocks above Apollo's temple and from there should be hurled down the precipices to her death. Ion himself, with a band of armed men, hurried away to see that this just sentence should be carried out.

But meanwhile some friend of Creusa who had been present at the feast had warned her of her danger, and Creusa, knowing that this was her only hope of safety, had hastened to the temple of Apollo, to the very altar of that god who had been, or who seemed to have been, of all others most unkind to her. Here she stayed, clinging to the altar in the hope that no one would dare to violate the holy place by dragging her away; and it was here that Ion found her.

So furious was Ion with her because of her attempt on his life that he refused to listen to her prayers for mercy and her appeals to the protection that ought to be afforded to her as a suppliant at the altar. To Ion it seemed that, since she had plotted against him, the servant of Apollo, in Apollo's own sanctuary, she could not possibly seek protection from the very god whom she had so insulted. His rage was so great that he would actually have torn her away from the altar by force, if, at this very moment, he had not been checked by the appearance of the Pythia, the chief prophetess of Apollo, through whose mouth the god himself reveals his mind to mortals. This was the same Pythia who had taken Ion into her arms when he was a baby and who had brought him up in the temple as though he were her own child. She loved Ion both because of the care she had taken of him and for himself, and now she came forward out of the inner sanctuary, partly because she wished to restrain him from the guilt of dragging away a suppliant from the altar and partly because the god had put it into her heart to reveal something which, up to this time, she had kept hidden. First she addressed Ion and said: 'My son (since to me you are like a son) I want you to go to Athens unstained by any sin. You must respect the altar of Apollo, in whose temple you have grown up as though he was your father. You must not use violence against one who has taken refuge here.'

But Ion, greatly as he respected and loved the Pythia, was still not persuaded by her words. 'How can it be wrong,' he said, 'to kill an enemy who has offended not only against me but against the god himself?'

'Then wait', said the Pythia, 'for Apollo has made it known to me that I must show you something which you have never seen before.' She then brought out from the inner sanctuary a cradle, made curiously out of woven willow twigs, and told him that this was the cradle in which she had received him when first she found him in the temple. It was a sight which made Ion glad, for, though he thought that he had discovered his father, he longed to know who his mother was, and it now seemed that in this cradle there might be some clue which would enable him to find her out. But when Creusa saw the cradle, her heart seemed to stop still, for she recognised it at once as the one in which she had so sadly laid her baby, when she had left him in the cave on the Acropolis of Athens. For a few moments she listened to the Pythia, who was describing to Ion exactly how he had been found and how, at the command of the god, she had until now revealed nothing about the cradle itself and the ornaments which it contained. And as she listened she became certain that the young man whom she had tried to murder and who was now so intent on killing her was indeed her own son. So she cried out joyfully, 'My son, my son!' and left the altar in order to embrace him.

Ion was now more bewildered than ever, but it was not long before Creusa convinced him. She told him of what he would find in the cradle, – of the coverlets which she, as a young girl, had woven and embroidered with the head of a gorgon, and of the golden serpents, the royal ornaments of the house of Erechtheus. And now Ion, with equal joy, embraced his mother; for all his life he had longed to find her. And now too he learned the final secret of his parentage, – that his father was none other than the god Apollo himself, who, though he had been unkind to his mother, had watched over the young life of the child and had now, by making a gift of him to Xuthus, established him as heir to a great Kingdom.

Creusa, for her part, was at last happy, since she had found the child of her own body who had been lost. As for Ion, his heart was full of a number of distinct feelings, some of joy and pride, others of a strange perplexity. Proud indeed he was to know that his mother was a queen and his father a great god; yet how strange to him and how incomprehensible seemed the workings of the divine powers! After so many changes and chances, could he even yet believe in the truth of what he had been told?

Yet before he left the temple his mind was set at rest. A vision of the goddess Athene appeared

D

to him and to Creusa and to the Pythia. Apollo himself, said Athene, would not appear, lest there should be blame for things done in the past; but in his name she declared that Ion was indeed his son and the son of Creusa. Apollo had given Ion to Xuthus as a friend might give to another friend who was childless one of his own sons to be his heir. So Ion was to rule in Athens and his mother would be content in the knowledge that, even though for the time others might think him the child of Xuthus, he was in reality her own child. And soon other children would be born to her and Xuthus, great leaders of men who would establish kingdoms in Achaea and in Doris. As for Ion himself he would have four sons who would give their names to the four tribes of the Athenians and later their descendants would cross the sea in their ships and found great cities on the coasts of Asia and on the islands in the sea. They would be a great people and would be called after Ion 'the Ionians', and in years to come would hold their great festival of singing and dancing and athletic games in Apollo's own island of Delos.

So they thanked the goddess for her comforting words and for her assurance of happiness and they prepared joyfully to return to Athens, where everything that the goddess had told them would be fulfilled.

ALCESTIS

ALCESTIS

THERE was a time when the god Apollo
greatly offended Zeus, his own father and
the father of gods and men. Apollo had a
child by a mortal woman and this child, Asclepius, when he grew up, became the greatest of
all physicians. He had learned from Apollo himself all the arts of healing and so well did he
practice them that he was able even to bring back
the dead to life. Zeus, thinking that no mortal
should possess such power, slew Asclepius with a
thunderbolt, and Apollo, in his anger at losing his
son, destroyed the giants called 'the Cyclopes'
who forge the thunderbolts for Zeus. Then Zeus
drove Apollo out from the company of the blessed
gods and sentenced him to work for one whole
year as a humble serving man among mortals on
earth.

Now the household in which Apollo was a
servant was that of Admetus, the great King of
Thessaly. It was a rich and hospitable household
and in Admetus Apollo found a master who was
generous and considerate to all his servants. Long
before Admetus was aware that he was sheltering
a great god, the divine power of Apollo made itself felt. For now the wealth of Admetus increased

continually; great harvests of golden corn came in from the rolling plains of Thessaly; the fruit trees bore more fruit than they had ever done; all things prospered, – the herds of fine horses, the cattle, the sheep, the olives and the vines. And Apollo himself, who watched the sheep, would play on a shepherd's pipe instead of his own lyre, and at the sound of his sweet music spotted lynxes would come out of the forests and lie down with the sheep to listen; lions too would troop down from the mountains and dappled fawns would come fearlessly with them. Then, when his year's service was over, Apollo wished still further to reward his host. He won for him a gift from the Fates themselves, and this was that, when the day fated for his death should arrive, Admetus might still live, provided that he could find some other person who would die instead of him.

But people are not as a rule willing to sacrifice their lives for others and it was far from easy for Admetus to find any person who would be willing to die, when the time came, in his place. He approached, amongst others, his aged father and pointed out to him that he could not in any case have very much longer to live and that, by fore-going the few years of life which were all that he could expect, he would win honour for himself besides conferring a great benefit on his son; as he was so old already, he could scarcely get much pleasure out of life and it might even be a positive advantage to him to die rather earlier than he might otherwise have done. But Admetus's old father was merely angry at the suggestion. He had already, he said, done a great deal for his son in resigning his kingdom to him while he was still alive; he had no wish at all to gain honour by departing from this life a minute earlier than he could help; and, so far from finding life a burden, he enjoyed it very much indeed. Much the same reply was given to Admetus by his mother and by various other old people, none of whom was prepared to recognise the force of the arguments which he employed.

Indeed there was only one person who was willing to help him and that was his beautiful young wife Alcestis. She had borne children to Admetus and she loved him dearly. She thought that, in any case, life without her husband would not be worth living and so she declared that, when the time came, she would allow Death to take her away so long as her husband was spared and left alive upon the earth.

Admetus accepted thc offer, though he still hoped that his friend Apollo might be able to arrange matters in such a way that this sacrifice of the woman whom he so dearly loved might not be necessary.

And so for some years Admetus and Alcestis lived undisturbed, but finally the day came which had been fixed by the Fates to be the day of death for Admetus. It was an earlier day than might have been expected, for Admetus's old parents were still alive, and he and his wife were still young. As this day drew near Alcestis began to feel its approach and to know that now the time had come for her to keep the promise that she had made. She began to grow weak in the body and in the head; she felt the powers of life fading away from her and she called to her husband and to her children to tell them that they must now say their last farewells, since Death himself would soon come to take her into the world of ghosts below the earth.

Now indeed Admetus was heartbroken and he wished that this gift from the gods had never been given to him or that, in any case, he had refused the noble offer which his wife had made. He had grown to love her more and more, and now she was to leave him for ever. He prayed to Apollo to help him, and indeed Apollo did all that he was able to do. When that grim creature Death, a power that is hated by gods and men, came to the palace of Admetus to take away Alcestis, Apollo met him and begged him to relent. But Death insisted upon his rights. He knew that a life was owing to him and he was going to take it. 'Nothing', he said to Apollo, 'can save her. And there is no champion either on earth or among the blessed gods who can rescue her from my hands.' So, having failed to win the goodwill of Death, Apollo went away, though he knew that Death, as will be seen, was boasting of more power than he really had.

Meanwhile inside the palace there was nothing but mourning and lamentation, for now Alcestis was very near the moment of dying. Her servants

had thronged round her, kissing her hands for the
last time and weeping helplessly for her; for she
had been a good and kind mistress to them and
there was not one of them who did not love her.
Next she said good-bye to her children and to her
husband. There were two small children, a boy
and a girl, and, though Alcestis loved them both,
she was most sad when she thought of the daughter who would be left motherless. The boy would
grow up to be a king and, as he grew up, his
father would protect him and support him; but
the girl would have no mother to dress her as a
bride when the time for her marriage came, or to
advise her in the new duties which would then
be hers. So Alcestis wept as she kissed her children
and she begged Admetus not to take a new wife
after she had gone, since a new wife might cause
him to forget or to neglect the children whom he
had already. As for Admetus it was easy for him
to give the promise which she asked of him, for
he loved her with his whole heart and he could
not bear the thought of ever marrying some other
woman. Now indeed he wished that it was he,
not she, who was to die, since death seemed to
him a better thing than a life spent in longing for
her. His tears fell fast as he promised her not only
that he would not marry again but that he would
mourn for her throughout his life and would keep
her image before his eyes, sleeping and waking,
until the time came when he too would have to
obey the summons of the fates and descend into
the bloodless world of the dead. Even as he spoke

to her, he saw that she was growing weaker and weaker; she smiled at him, but there was a mist in front of her eyes; he cried out to her, begging her, uselessly enough, to stay with him. But the moment fixed unchangeably by the Fates had now been reached. The eyes of Alcestis were closed in death. Admetus and his whole household wept and lamented for her as for one whom they would never see again moving among them in her gracious and loving way.

And now, while the body of Alcestis was being prepared for the tomb in which it was to be laid, while the children were weeping for their mother and while Admetus, distraught with his own grief, was scarcely able to attempt to comfort them, it was suddenly announced to him that a friend of his had arrived at the palace and was asking to receive hospitality. This friend was the hero Hercules who was still, because of the anger of Hera, the wife of Zeus, forced to serve the cowardly King Eurystheus for whom he was performing those great labours which were to make him famous for ever. Just now he was travelling northward to the land of Thrace where he was to fight for and to win the terrible man-eating horses of the Thracian King Diomedes. As his way lay through Thessaly he had determined to visit Admetus, who had long been his friend and in whose hospitable house he had often eaten and drunk in times past. He knew nothing of the calamity which had now fallen upon this house and, had he known of it, he would never have come at a

moment so ill-suited for entertaining guests. As
it was he was weary from his journey and, since
his appetite was as prodigious as his strength, he
was looking forward to a great feast and long
draughts of wine and the music and singing which
he expected.

Admetus himself knew that Hercules would
not easily find elsewhere the hospitality that his
own palace could afford. In happier days he
himself had enjoyed feasting with the hero and
now, when, because of his grief, it was impossible
for him to eat meat or drink wine, he still did not
wish to turn a friend away from his doors. So,
when Hercules came to greet him and noticed
on all sides sad faces and the signs of mourning,
Admetus disguised the real truth from him and,
in order to show kindness to his guest, pretended
that, though indeed there had been a death in
the house, it was not a death that concerned him
nearly. 'My dear friend,' he said, 'as you can
see, I have to attend a funeral today and so I
cannot join you in the feast. But you must not
leave this house without being entertained'; and
he gave orders to his servants to prepare a room
for Hercules in that part of the palace which was
reserved for guests and which was at some distance from the rooms where the mourners were
gathered together and where the body of Alcestis
was being prepared for burial.

At first Hercules objected. 'I cannot disturb
you,' he said, 'at a time of mourning. Let me go
on my way now and visit you later, when I am

THE DYING ALCESTIS

coming back from Thrace.' But Admetus would hear of no excuse. Even in his own misery he wished to be hospitable to his friends; and so Hercules was taken in to the guest chamber and there a large meal was prepared for him. Admetus himself, with his children and those of the servants who were not waiting upon Hercules, retired to another part of the palace and mourned for the dead Alcestis. Later, when the proper rites had been performed, they took up the body and, in a sad procession, carried it out of the palace and set it down in the tomb that had been built for it outside the city.

Meanwhile Hercules, quite ignorant of what was really taking place in the house, was occupied entirely in enjoying himself. He crowned his head with garlands and sat down eagerly to the great banquet that was set before him. He ate plentifully of the meat and drank bowl after bowl of the dark wine. The more he ate and drank the more pleased he felt with himself and soon he began to shout out songs, unmusically enough, since, though he was a great warrior and the strongest man of his time, he had little knowledge of the arts of singing and of playing upon the lyre. The servants who waited upon him looked on with disgust at his drunken revelling and listened with a kind of dismay to his bellowing and howling. All their thoughts were with their dead mistress and, in the general grief, they felt affronted at the sight of this unseasonable and tipsy merriment. They did their best to hide their tears, for Admetus had strictly ordered them to do so, but it was impossible for them to smile or laugh or look cordially on the uncouth revelling of this insatiable guest.

In the end Hercules himself noticed the sour looks and downcast eyes of those who were waiting on him. He seized hold of one of the servants and dragged him to the table. 'Drink, drink, my good fellow!' he shouted, 'and get rid of that miserable look of yours. We all know the pains of life, but there are pleasures too. While there is wine to drink and while there are women to love, we can at least be merry from time to time.' And he thrust a great bowl of wine into the servant's unwilling hand.

Now the servant could contain his feelings no longer. 'Indeed,' he said, 'I know all this that you say. But we cannot be happy in this house at this moment. Our dear mistress, the wife of Admetus, is dead and is even now being carried to her tomb.'

This news made Hercules sober at once. 'How terrible it is,' he said, 'that on such a day as this I should have been revelling and feasting and singing in my friend's house. But why did Admetus hide this from me? Why did he not let me share his sorrow?'

'He wished to give you pleasure,' said the servant, 'and I have disobeyed him in telling you the true position of this house. My master is a hospitable man and he wanted you to be happy and refreshed even though he himself was miserable.'

'Then,' said Hercules, 'since this noble man has treated me so nobly I shall return him good for good. You must tell me where the tomb is and I shall go to it. Then I shall wait in ambush until Death himself comes to drink the blood-offerings and to carry away his victim to the lower world. When I see him coming, I shall leap out on him and grip him in my strong arms. Let him strain and wrestle as he will, I shall hold him fast and shall never let him go until he gives up Alcestis to me so that I can bring her back to this palace and to her husband. And, if I fail to find Death at the tomb, I shall go down to the world of ghosts, the Kingdom of Pluto and Persephone, and even from there I shall bring Alcestis back.'

So Hercules spoke and the servants told him in what direction he might find the tomb. Few of them had any belief in what he had said that he would accomplish, for his words seemed more like the boasting of a drunken man than like a plan that could really be carried out.

Nevertheless Hercules set out on his way to the tomb and, soon after he had gone, Admetus himself and those who had accompanied him came back to the palace from the funeral. They had laid the body in the tomb and had made the proper sacrifices of black cattle and of black sheep to the gods below the earth. Then, with wailing and lamentation, they had returned. And now the grief of Admetus was boundless, for he had looked, he thought, for the last time of all on the face of his wife whom he loved and who had loved him so much that she had died for him. Now every sight in his great palace was painful to him, for everything reminded him of her, – the chair where she used to sit, the bed where she slept, the courtyards and gardens where she had walked and talked with him. Now he cursed the gift which Apollo had won for him from the Fates. Though he was indeed alive himself there was no pleasure left in living without the woman who had given her life for his. Nor could he even live in honour, since he was ashamed to have escaped death himself by having accepted the sacrifice of another's life.

So he sat down in front of his rich palace, miserable and wretched as he had never been, nor could any words be found to comfort him. All that day he remained there until at sunset it was seen that two figures were approaching. One of them was without doubt the hero Hercules, for there could be no other man with so tall and stout a frame. He was leading by the hand a woman whose body and face were entirely covered in a thick cloak and veil. Soon they stood in front of Admetus and first Hercules reproached his friend for not having let him know of his terrible loss. 'I still feel ashamed,' he said, 'to have feasted and made merry in your house at the very time when you were burying your wife.'

'I too,' said Admetus, 'would have been ashamed if I had turned you away from my doors and let you go on your way without comfort and refreshment.'

'Indeed you acted nobly,' said Hercules, 'and now let me tell you that this grief of yours will not last for ever. Time heals everything.'

'Nothing,' said Admetus, 'can put an end to my sorrow. Time cannot cure it. It can only be healed in death.'

'Be that as it may,' Hercules replied, 'I have one request to make of you before I set out again on my journey. Keep this woman for me in your house and let me see her on my return. Today I won her in a wrestling match.'

But Admetus turned his head away. 'Ask me for anything else,' he said, 'but not this. How can I, who have just lost the best woman in the world, keep another woman in my house? Indeed I could not do it.'

'Yet you would be wise to do so,' said Hercules, 'and I still ask you to do this for me as a favour.'

Admetus glanced at the woman and then he looked quickly away. 'You are asking me for something impossible,' he said, 'for her bearing and her stature are like those of my dead wife. Every time I saw her my sorrow would be renewed. I could not bear it for her to be in my palace where, as it is, everything reminds me of Alcestis.'

'Then just look once in her face,' said Hercules, 'and after that I will ask nothing else of you.'

So, though reluctantly, Admetus turned his head towards the veiled woman and the woman drew back the veil from her face. What Admetus saw was nothing strange and nothing that he had

E

expected. He saw the face of his own wife Alcestis who had come back to him from the dead. For some moments, while he stared at her in amazement and fixed his eyes upon that smile of hers which he knew so well, he could not believe in his eyes, nor could he form any conception of his own happiness. Then Hercules told him of how he had wrestled with Death himself and how he had won back the noble woman who had been for a short time in Death's strong hand.

So Admetus received his wife back again and now life was happier for both of them than it had ever been before. As for Hercules, he went on his way northward, for he still had other labours to perform.

HIPPOLYTUS

HIPPOLYTUS

THERE were many famous deeds done by Theseus, the great King of Athens, when he was a young man. Among them was an expedition which he made with his friend Hercules against the Amazons, a race of warlike women. Theseus carried off the Queen of the Amazons and by her he became the father of a son whom he called Hippolytus.

Some time later he married Phaedra, the daughter of Minos, King of Crete. With her he lived happily and two children were born who were, so Theseus hoped, to become kings of Athens after his death. Meanwhile Hippolytus, his first son, was being brought up not in Athens, but in the town across the water, Troizen, where Theseus himself had been born and where he had spent his childhood. Theseus left Hippolytus in the care of his own grandfather. This was the wise and good King Pittheus of Troizen, whose daughter Aethra had been the mother of Theseus. It was not certain who was the father of Theseus. Some said that it was Aigeus, King of Athens; others that it was the great god of the sea, Poseidon, and that this god had promised Theseus that in the course of his life he could make three prayers to him and each of these prayers would be granted.

Under the care of Pittheus Hippolytus grew up to be a young man of whom any father might be proud. He was strong and handsome; he was wise and moderate in his behaviour; he was a great rider and huntsman, a lover of all athletic sports. More than all things he worshipped the virgin goddess Artemis, herself a great huntress and one who chiefly preferred those men and women who enjoy the green woods and the sport of the chase more than the pleasures of making love. So much did Artemis love Hippolytus that she would go with him on his hunting expeditions and, though she would never let him see her face, she would speak to him and he would hear her voice; she would be at his side, and he could feel her presence. And for the young Hippolytus this was the happiest of all lives, to spend his time in hunting and in manly exercise and every day to converse with the great goddess whom he honoured and adored.

But by living this kind of life he made another goddess jealous of him. This was Aphrodite, the proud goddess of love, through whose power everything that lives on the earth, in the air and in the waters, has its being and perpetuates its own kind. Though he was himself the especial favourite of Artemis and it was in her company that he most delighted, Hippolytus respected the other gods and goddesses and paid them the honours that were due to them. Aphrodite alone he neglected to honour, for nothing in his life had

HIPPOLYTUS AND ARTEMIS

anything to do with the love that exists between men and women; instead all his pleasure was in training horses, in hurling the javelin, and in the company of the huntress Artemis.

The gods, like men, are pleased when they receive praise and angry if they feel themselves insulted. This was the case with Aphrodite. She was angry when she saw the offerings upon the altars of Artemis and no offerings upon her own. She determined to be revenged upon Hippolytus and she thought out a cruel plan by which she would destroy not only him but others as well.

It happened that Theseus, in order to atone for a sin which he had committed, had been ordered by an oracle to leave Athens and spend one year away from his own city. So, with his wife Phaedra, he crossed the water to the nearby kingdom of Troizen where he was made welcome by the old Pittheus and by the young man Hippolytus. It was now that Aphrodite proceeded to carry out her plan of vengeance.

For her it was easy; indeed some of the work had been done already, since, a little time previously, Hippolytus had come to Athens to visit his father and to take part in the holy mysteries of Eleusis, and, while he was there, Phaedra had seen him and, though it was against her will, she had fallen in love with him. How could she help it, when Aphrodite, the goddess of love herself, forced her to do so? And now, when she was actually living in Troizen and seeing Hippolytus every day, the love that Phaedra felt for the young man became greater and greater. She began to waste away in a sickness of which no one knew the cause. And all this was by the will of Aphrodite, who wished Theseus to believe that Hippolytus, though he was entirely guiltless, was conspiring to gain the love of his wife; then, so Aphrodite planned, Theseus would call down upon his son one of the curses which his father Poseidon was bound to fulfil. Phaedra too would have to die, but to her fate the goddess was indifferent so long as her own revenge was satisfied.

There was a day when Theseus was absent from the palace of Troizen, though before evening he was to return. It was this day that Aphrodite chose to destroy Hippolytus. Her eyes were upon him as he came back on this day from hunting. His friends and his servants were surrounding him as they approached the palace, singing, as they came, a hymn to Artemis. No one, except Aphrodite, knew that this was the last day that ever Hippolytus would go hunting in the forests of Troizen.

Standing in front of the palace were two statues, one of Artemis and one of Aphrodite. Now, as Hippolytus approached the palace, he knelt down, as he always did, before the statue of Artemis. In the green woods he had found a cool meadow, a lonely place where no shepherd had ever fed his flocks nor had the grass ever felt the stroke of iron; only the bees crossed and re-crossed this virgin meadow in the spring. Here he had picked flowers and made them into a wreath, and now he brought the wreath and offered it reverently to the statue of the virgin goddess who was his friend, thanking her for her kindness to him and praying her that his life might for ever be as happy as now it was. After he had made his offering he rose to go into the palace, but first an old servant of his, one who knew him well and loved him, asked permission to give him some advice. Hippolytus gladly gave him this permission.

'Do you not know, then,' said the old man, 'that when a person is proud and exclusive people dislike him, but they are grateful when a person speaks kindly and politely to them?'

'Of course,' Hippolytus replied. 'Everyone hates arrogance; and, as for being polite, it is no trouble to one and it gives other people pleasure.'

'And do you not think,' asked the old man, 'that the gods also think as we do about this?'

'No doubt they do,' said Hippolytus.

'Then,' said the old man, 'will you not take my advice and say one word of greeting to that other great goddess at the gate, the goddess Aphrodite?'

But Hippolytus would not. 'There are different tastes,' he said, 'both among gods and men. And as for me, I have no taste for a goddess men worship in the night, away from the race tracks and the bright mountain air where my life is spent so happily.'

So, after giving instructions to his servants to rub down the horses and get them ready to be yoked to his chariot in the afternoon, Hippolytus and his young friends went on into the palace where their meal was prepared for them.

The old servant stayed behind and bowed low before the statue of Aphrodite. 'O great goddess,' he prayed to her, be merciful to a young man who, because of his youth, speaks foolishly. I beg you to have pity on him and to understand him, as I do. For gods ought to be wiser than men and more understanding.'

But this prayer had no effect at all upon the angry heart of Aphrodite.

All this time, and for many days past, Phaedra had kept away from company and had remained inside her room restless, fevered and sick because of the passion for Hippolytus which the goddess had put into her heart. She would not touch the food that was offered to her; she did not trouble to dress or to adorn her golden hair; neither music nor conversation gave her any pleasure; for music reminded her of love and in no conversation could she bear to reveal her own guilty thoughts. Sometimes she would be half out of her mind and would speak deliriously. At these times all her talk would be of the beating of horses' hooves, of Thessalian javelins and of the cool glades in the forest where the wild beasts were encircled by baying hounds and by the bands of huntsmen. At other times she would come to herself and then she would wonder in misery what she could have done to make her so unhappy, how this madness could have come over her and which one of the gods it could be who was so persecuting her with desires from which she shrank away. She was attended only by her old nurse, who loved her, but who had no notion of what was the real nature of her disease.

On this morning, restless as ever, Phaedra had asked that her couch should be carried out of the palace into the open air, although wherever she was, whether indoors or out, her suffering found no relief and her tired brain enjoyed no relaxation. Her nurse was with her and, in the light of day, could see how wasted were her mistress's features, how wild was her eye, how desperate the whole manner of her behaviour. And for this terrible distress of mind there seemed to be no reason. Phaedra was a queen and lacked nothing; her husband, Theseus, loved her; she had children who were to be kings. If only she would say what was the matter with her, it would be easier, so her nurse thought, to find some way of helping her. Yet, though she questioned her over and over again, Phaedra would give no answer that could account for her unhappy state. All that she would say was that she was resolved to die and that it would be better for her and for everyone else if indeed she could die. Her nurse attempted to make her see how wrong she was to entertain such an idea.

'If you were to die,' she said, 'what would happen to your children? Without you they might lose their place in their father's affection. Someone else might be chosen to rule in Athens.

Remember that Theseus has another son, Hippolytus.'

Now, at the name of Hippolytus, Phaedra could not help crying out aloud. She begged and implored her nurse never again to mention that name in front of her. But the nurse, though still she could not guess why it was that Phaedra had cried out so despairingly at the young man's name, began to question her more closely and, in the end, weak and tired as she was, longing too to free her own heart of the burden of its secret, Phaedra confessed that she had fallen in love with Hippolytus and it was for this reason that her mind and body were being destroyed.

Her nurse was horrified at what she heard. Her mistress, she knew, was wise and good. How could it be that she could even think of betraying her husband and of losing her own good name?

As for Phaedra, now that she had been able to say aloud truthfully what it was that had been torturing her, she became calmer in mind and began to explain exactly what had happened. She hated, she said, those women who are false to their husbands; for they bring shame not only upon themselves but upon their children after them. And so, when first she found that she had fallen in love, she had tried to cover up her feelings and to conquer them by the power of reason. This she had not been able to do, and so now, since there was no help in reason, she was determined to die, for in this way alone she could keep an honourable name for herself and be honoured afterwards by her husband and by her children.

She spoke sadly and she spoke with resolution; but her nurse, who loved her, was resolved above all things to save her mistress's life. So now she began to argue with her. 'There is nothing strange,' she said, 'or unheard of about falling in love. Many people before now have fallen in love with those who were not their wives or their husbands. Even the gods, according to the old stories, have done so. It is not really possible for anyone in this life to be absolutely virtuous. All that one can be expected to do is to look virtuous and to hide one's sins. Certainly it is ridiculous to put an end to your life, just because some god has put it into your heart to fall in love with the wrong person. It would be much better to enjoy your love. Maybe it is wrong, but it is better to enjoy yourself than to kill yourself.'

Phaedra was glad to hear such an argument, even though she knew that it was a wicked one and untrue. And now the nurse began to beg her mistress to leave matters to her. There were magic spells, she said, which might be used in such cases; nothing, in fact, was impossible.

Such words as these swayed the weak mind of Phaedra. She began to hope that somehow, though she did not know how this could be, she might escape from her pain and still, again in some way that she could not understand, remain honest. Partly she trusted her nurse and partly she distrusted her. She might say some word to Hippolytus himself. That would be a dreadful thing. Yet, if Hippolytus were to listen to the nurse's words, it might not be so dreadful. So, with a mind divided between hope and fear, between shame and desperation, Phaedra watched her nurse go inside the palace. At the gate of the palace the old nurse paused and made her prayers to Aphrodite. 'Lady of the Sea,' she said, 'help me and let me gain for my mistress the things that she desires.' She did not know that Aphrodite was determined to destroy not only Hippolytus but Phaedra as well. She did not remember how often it has happened that love, which can be so gentle, has utterly destroyed those who have felt it in its full and destructive force. For not the thunderbolt itself can be more heavy on men than the arrow of Aphrodite.

Now there was a time of waiting, but soon Phaedra heard from inside the palace the sound of a voice raised in anger. Shame and terror gave her strength. She sprang up from her couch and went to the door of the palace where she could listen to the words that were being spoken inside. She found that everything which she had most feared had taken place. Her nurse had approached Hippolytus, had first made him swear a solemn oath that he would keep secret what she had to say, and had then told him that Phaedra, the wife of his father, was dying for love of him. If the old woman had expected that Hippolytus would feel any sympathy for such a story, she was wholly mistaken. Hippolytus felt outraged by what he had heard, and the words to which Phaedra was now listening were words of hatred and contempt for herself and for all other women in existence. His rage was boundless. 'Why,' he shouted out, 'did the gods ever allow women to exist? Surely there could have been some other way of getting children and then men could have lived happily without wives. For all wives are vain, expensive, treacherous and deceitful.' Turning to the nurse he told her that her words were so horrible that he felt unclean simply to have listened to them. If he had not foolishly bound himself by his oath, he would have told Theseus the whole disgraceful story. As it was, so long as Theseus was absent, he also would stay away from home. Nor would he ever cease hating women; for until someone could teach them modesty and self-control, he could never learn to feel anything for them but contempt.

Phaedra had heard enough. Now that her feelings had been betrayed and had been trodden underfoot she knew that there could be no end except death to her unendurable pain. She hurried to her room, determined to take her own life. But before doing this dreadful thing she would secretly revenge herself upon the innocent man who was the cause of her death, and, in revenging herself, she would, or so she thought, preserve her own good name. She wrote a letter in which she told a story that was the opposite of the truth. In this letter she bade farewell to her husband and wrote that the reason for her death was Hippolytus, who had forced his own love upon her against her will. Then she looked her last upon the light of Troizen which had seen her unhappiness. She fastened a rope about her neck and, holding in her hand the letter that was to avenge her, she hanged herself.

It was not long before her death was discovered, and now the whole palace rang with the cries and lamentations of her servants, who knew nothing of what had caused her death, and of her nurse, who knew only too well. It was in the middle of these lamentations that Theseus himself returned. He was amazed to find no one to greet him in front of the palace gates and to hear, instead of words of welcome, the sound of mourning and of grief. Had anything, he wondered, happened to his children or to the old King Pittheus while he had been away? But soon the gates were opened and he saw what had really happened. He saw the dead body of the wife whom he loved, and he saw that it was she herself who had taken her own life. 'O my wife,' he cried out in his insupportable grief, 'you dearest of all things to me and best of all women that the sun shines upon, how could you have left me alone? How could you have left our children motherless?'

For some time his grief was too great to allow him to think. Then he noticed that there was a letter in his wife's dead hand. 'Perhaps,' he thought, 'the poor creature has written in her pain to say good-bye to me and to leave her last wishes for the children. Indeed I shall do everything that she could ask me to do.'

But when he took the letter from her hand and read the words that it contained, his mind was overwhelmed with horror and with rage. Now he believed (and how could he help believing it?) that his own son Hippolytus, the son of whom he had been so proud, the son in whose honour and goodness he had had complete faith, was guilty of the deepest ingratitude and of the most unspeakable crime. Theseus raised his hands to heaven and prayed to his father, Poseidon, the god of the sea. 'O Poseidon,' he cried, 'my father, you who gave me the right to pray to you three times and to have my prayers granted, now grant me one of these prayers. Destroy my son Hippolytus. Let him not live to see the sun set on this day!'

There were some in Theseus's company who begged him to call back this prayer again, to wait until he was sure that he had found out the truth; but to Theseus the truth seemed sure and certain. No evidence could be more convincing than the letter which he had found in the dead woman's hand.

And now, with no knowledge of what had happened and what was about to happen, Hippolytus himself came to see his father. He had heard a cry of grief and he hastened to see what it could be that had caused it. He stopped still in astonishment when he saw the dead body of Phaedra, but he was more astonished still when he saw his father look so angrily upon him, when he heard his father charge him with a dreadful

crime which, as Hippolytus knew well, he could
never have committed. What was he to say? He
had sworn a great oath by all the gods to the
nurse that he would never reveal what she had
said to him. And even in his great danger, he
would never break his oath. All he could do was
to protest his innocence, to remind his father of
how pure and blameless his life had always been,
of how he had never yet failed in his duty to gods
and to men. But to Theseus all this seemed evidence not of innocence, but of a disgusting hypo-
crisy. Roughly he told his son to leave his
presence and never again to set foot in the land of
Troizen or in the land of Athens. So, even if
Poseidon did not destroy him, he would die
miserably in exile, since no good man would
receive him into his house.

So Hippolytus prepared to leave the court and
to leave the land where he had lived so happily
and the forests in which he had hunted in the
company of the goddess whom he loved. Bitterly
grieved he was at his departure into exile, but
more grieved still to find that his father could
believe him guilty of something which he had not
done and which his noble nature would never
have allowed him to do.

Theseus was left alone, mourning for his wife
and meditating upon the punishment which, he
thought, he had so righteously inflicted on his
son. But before the day was over he was to hear of
how Poseidon had granted his prayer and of how
greatly mistaken he had been in his judgment.

First, after some hours had passed, came one of the servants of Hippolytus with the news that his master was on the point of death. He was still just breathing and still able to speak, but life was ebbing from him fast so that he could not live until the sun set. When he heard this news, Theseus gave thanks to his father Poseidon and asked how this just punishment had fallen upon the young man.

Hippolytus's servant told him the story: after leaving his father's presence, Hippolytus had gone down to the sea shore and with him had gone a company of the young men of Troizen, his friends whom he loved and whom he was sad to leave behind. Hippolytus had mounted his chariot drawn by fine horses which he had trained and bred himself. Then, while his friends wept to see him go, he had taken the reins in his hand and prayed to Zeus, the King of the gods, that, whether he lived or died, one day his father would know that he had wronged him. And so he set forward along the road leading northward, the road where in the past Theseus himself had performed great deeds when he was a young man, killing evil men and robbers who had then infested it. With Hippolytus went his servants, running by the side of the chariot.

There was a place where the road ran along the sea shore. When they reached this place they heard a roaring sound, like thunder, rising from the ground. The horses raised their heads, pricked up their ears and began to sweat with terror. And now, looking towards the sea, they saw an enormous wave towering up so high that it hid from their view the rocks and mountains at the further side of the bay. The wave rushed towards the shore where the trembling horses stood, with Hippolytus holding the reins firmly in his experienced hands. It broke with a crash and roar of water, and, out of the white foam and circling eddies where it broke there arose a great bull, a fierce and monstrous shape, which began to bellow aloud, filling all the land with the noise it made. The horses panicked and began to bolt. Hippolytus, seeing that all his strength would be needed, knotted the loose ends of the reins behind his back. Leaning back upon them and tugging with his hands he tried to control the horses, maddened as they were with fear. Yet all his knowledge of horses and all his skill in their management could not help him. If he tried to steer their course on to smoother ground, then the bull would suddenly appear in front of them, and they would swerve away from him in their terror. And then the bull would run silently alongside them, edging them upon the rocks, till, finally, he forced a wheel against a huge stone. The axle broke; the chariot was overturned; and now the maddened horses dragged the body of their master, still entangled in the reins, hither and thither over the pointed rocks that cut into his flesh. Still Hippolytus cried out to them, but the horses would not listen to the well-known voice that so often they had obeyed. Somehow or other, in the end, Hippolytus managed to free himself from the reins. His servants hurried up to him where he lay alone and broken upon the shore. The horses and that fearful monster of a bull had disappeared out of sight. As for Hippolytus, there was little life left in him.

So his servant, sad and angry at his master's fate, told the story to Theseus, and, though he was a servant speaking to a King, he dared to say that he would never believe that Hippolytus was a wicked man, no not if all the women in the world were to hang themselves and to leave messages behind them after their deaths.

Theseus was unmoved. 'Bring the young man before me,' he said. 'He will recognize now that the gods themselves have shown him to be guilty.'

Yet the gods, or at least one of them, now showed Theseus that his son had been innocent. Hardly had he finished speaking to the servant who had told him of how his curse had been fulfilled, when he heard another voice in the air above him and looking upwards, he saw, with reverence and with fear, the great goddess Artemis herself, the friend of Hippolytus. In calm words she told to Theseus the whole story of his wife's unhappy passion, of how his son, because he would never break a promise, had been unable to defend himself, and had therefore been wrongfully done to death by Poseidon, who was bound to answer the prayer that Theseus had made to him. All these things had come about through the anger and jealousy of Aphrodite. There was

no help for them, nor could Artemis herself have
done anything to save the mortal who was her
servant and whom she loved.

And now, when Theseus realised the terrible
mistake of which he had been guilty, his heart
was broken within him. How could he ever be
forgiven for the wrong which he had done to his
own son? How could he ever forgive himself?
As he thought with agony of what the goddess
was telling him, Hippolytus himself, now near the
moment of his death, was carried into the palace.
His beautiful body was bruised and torn and
bleeding. Pain leapt along his limbs at every
movement of his friends and servants who were
bearing him as gently as they could. But he felt
immediately the presence in that place of the
goddess Artemis and he listened to her as she told
him of how Aphrodite had plotted against him
and of how his father had been deceived. She
told him to forgive his father for what he had
done, since his mind had been led astray, and
then she said good-bye to him, since no god or
goddess can look on dying men and now Hippolytus was very near to death. She promised him
that his name would live for ever and that for
ever afterwards the maidens of the land of Troizen
would make offerings of the tresses of their hair at
his tomb before they wedded their husbands.
Then, since she could do no more for him, she
left him to die. But, before he died, his father
Theseus begged him for his forgiveness, and
Hippolytus gladly gave his forgiveness to him.

For both father and son had been powerless to fight against the power of the goddess Aphrodite who had been determined to destroy the one of them and to leave the other desolate.

IPHIGENEIA

IPHIGENEIA

THE army and navy that sailed from Greece against Troy to sack the city and to bring back Helen, whom Paris had treacherously stolen from her husband, was the greatest force that had ever been gathered together for war. It was commanded by Agamemnon, King of golden Mycenae, with his brother Menelaus, the husband of Helen and the King of Sparta. Ships in their hundreds and warriors in their thousands assembled in the harbour of Aulis, off the east coast of Greece. From there they were to cross the Aegean sea, force a landing on the coast of Troy and, they hoped, soon bring down that proud city and its defenders to the dust.

But the gods willed otherwise. More than ten years were to pass and many of the greatest of the Greeks were to lose their lives before their purpose would be accomplished and before the flames would spread along the long walls and surge above the high towers of Troy.

Even the very outset of the expedition was unpropitious and, for a time, seemed impossible. For when the great host had gathered together at Aulis and each man in it was ready and eager to cross the sea and win glory and booty in the fighting that lay ahead, long and valuable months went by while the ships lay motionless in the harbour and the army remained inactive on the land. Instead of the winds that would have taken them over the sea and which were to be expected at that time of year, the winds that blew were mostly contrary or else there was no wind at all. And so the ship's hawsers, sagging in the water, began to rot away. As for the warriors in the army, they amused themselves as best they could in games and exercises. You might have seen there great Ajax, the biggest man of them all, sitting on the ground playing draughts, with his huge shield and spear at his side; or that fierce fighter Diomedes hurling the discus from his strong arm. Achilles, the fleet-footed and the greatest warrior of them all, would race in full armour against a four horse chariot team, matching his own strength against the strength of finely bred horses and outdistancing them as he sped over the sand and shingle of the shore.

So the warriors diverted themselves; but the men in the army, and soon even the great champions themselves grew tired of the delay and of the purposelessness of this empty waiting for a wind that never came. Food became more difficult to obtain. Inactivity in a great army usually breeds unrest and there were many who now began to wish that they had never left their homes to sail on an expedition to recover another man's wife. It was even suggested that the whole great armament should break up and return, since it seemed that the gods were averse to its ever setting out to its destination.

It was natural that this mood in the army should worry and perplex the leaders, and particularly the two sons of Atreus, Agamemnon and Menelaus. For it was for the sake of Menelaus that this force had been gathered together and Menelaus himself was resolved to recover his wife and to avenge himself upon Paris who had stolen her away from him. As for Agamemnon, he loved his brother and was himself a proud and ambitious man. It was he who was in supreme command of this great army and navy of the Greeks. He could not bear to see such a force disbanded before something noteworthy and glorious had been achieved.

And so, in their anxiety, the sons of Atreus consulted the prophet Calchas, a man who, from dreams, from the flight of birds and from examining the entrails of animals that had been sacrificed, was able to know the will of the gods and to declare it to men. When Calchas was asked for his opinion, he refused at first to give it, saying that he feared that his words would give offence. But the sons of Atreus pressed him hard and in the end the prophet spoke. He said that the goddess Artemis, who was worshipped in Aulis, was angry with the Greeks. It was she who prevented the winds from blowing and her anger would never be appeased until she had received the sacrifice that she demanded. Nor was this sacrifice a goat or an ox; it was something far different. What the goddess desired (nor would she be contented with anything less) was that Agamemnon's own daughter, Iphigeneia, should be brought to Aulis and should there be struck down with the knife, like an animal, at her altar.

When Agamemnon heard the words of Calchas he wished that he had never made any enquiry into the will of heaven. For how could a father kill his own daughter, and a daughter, moreover, whom he loved more than all his other children? In his palace at Mycenae it had always been Iphigeneia who was the first to welcome him and to throw her arms about his neck when he returned from hunting or from travel. She had always been the one to lead the singing and the dancing at his feasts and it was her sweet voice and her graceful movements that delighted him more than all the joys that he had known at home. He had found it difficult to bear the thought that one day his favourite child would have to leave him to marry some great king among the Greeks. But this was nothing compared to what Calchas had ordained. For, if he were to obey the will of the gods declared by the prophet, she would leave him finally and for ever, and he, who loved her most, would be her murderer. He shrank from a thought so dreadful and from a deed so wicked.

Menelaus could well understand his brother's feelings since he also had a daughter, Hermione, whom he had left at home when he set out from Sparta. Yet such was his rage against Paris and his determination to avenge himself upon the

Trojans that he was willing to accept the words which Calchas had spoken and he urged his brother to carry out, however painful it might be, the will of Artemis. For, he said, unless this sacrifice were made, Troy would never be conquered and the great expedition of all the Greeks would become a mockery. Trojans in future, emboldened by the success of Paris, would be free to sail the seas and to carry off the wives of the leaders of the Greeks. And then there was the army itself. The soldiers were willing to risk their lives for Greece; but they expected that their generals also should be willing to sacrifice for the sake of the army anything, however near or dear.

In this way Menelaus and Calchas tried to turn the mind of Agamemnon away from the horror which he felt at the deed which he was called upon to do, and in the end they were successful in their endeavours. Agamemnon bowed to the will of the goddess, to the needs of the army and to his brother's prayers. He consented to send for his loved daughter from his house and to sacrifice her in Aulis on the altar of Artemis.

Yet it would be impossible for him to send a message to his wife Clytemnestra, telling her the sad truth. No mother would consent to let her daughter go from home to her death. Nor would Clytemnestra be at all swayed by the misfortunes of the army or by the desires of her brother-in-law, Menelaus. For Clytemnestra regarded her sister Helen as a wicked and dishonest wife who had brought shame upon her family. She would certainly not be willing to sacrifice her own daughter in order to bring Helen home again. And so Agamemnon deceived his wife by sending her a letter in which he asked her to bring Iphigeneia to Aulis, not for the real and dreadful purpose which he had in mind, but in order that she might be married to Achilles, the best of all the Greeks. He did not tell Achilles that he had used his name in order to entice his daughter from the shelter of her home; for Achilles was a proud and honourable man. He might agree that the sacrifice was necessary for the good of the army, but he would never himself take part in a plot to deceive others.

When Clytemnestra received her husband's letter she was full of joy. She had expected that by this time he would have crossed the sea to Troy and she was glad that she would see him again before he was plunged into the dangers of the war. She was happy too that her daughter was to be married to so great a man as Achilles, for of all the Greeks he was the one whom she would have chosen to be her son-in-law. And so, as soon as she had received the letter, she made all the haste she could. Fine horses were brought from the stables and harnessed to the chariot that would carry her and Iphigeneia to Aulis. Few soldiers had been left behind at Mycenae, but these too accompanied the great ladies as an escort. The dresses for the wedding were carefully packed, and so the two women took the road northwards to the camp of the Greeks, expecting to find there not death, but happiness. They travelled fast and arrived, as will be seen, even earlier than Agamemnon had expected them.

Agamemnon, when he had sent the letter to his wife and had taken the dreadful decision to become the murderer of his daughter, almost at once began to repent of what he had done. His nights were vexed with fearful dreams and in the daytime his daughter's face and her noble nature were always present to his mind's eye. He could not bear to follow to the end the course which he had taken, and yet he was too cowardly to say so openly, since he was afraid of Menelaus and of Calchas and of Odysseus, the King of Ithaca, a great warrior and the man of most resource among the Greeks. These three were, so far, the only ones who knew of the intended sacrifice, but Agamemnon was afraid to stand out against them, for, though he was a great king, he was a weak man. So, instead of refusing openly to do what Calchas had required him to do, he acted secretly. He wrote another letter to his wife, telling her that, for reasons which he did not give, the marriage of their daughter could not take place at this time and instructing her to go back again to Mycenae without visiting the Greek camp. He gave the letter to an old servant, a man who was devoted to his family and to Clytemnestra herself, and, to make sure that this old servant would hurry on his way and do all in his power to prevent Iphigeneia ever coming to Aulis, he took him into his confidence and told him the true

G

reason why this innocent girl was being lured
from her home. The good old servant was horrified at what he heard and promised to make all
the speed he could upon the road; for he loved
both his master and his mistress and he would
gladly have laid down his life to prevent the
dreadful deed which was now so close at hand.

But the letter was never to reach the hand to
which it was addressed. As the servant was leaving Agamemnon's tent he was accosted by Menelaus, who knew his brother's mind and was
suspicious of it. Menelaus seized upon the old
man, snatched the letter from him and tore it
open. He saw that Agamemnon was intending
to go back upon his promise and he rushed inside
the tent in order to reproach him for what he
regarded as his treachery. Angry words were
spoken between the brothers, neither being willing to give way to the other, but their quarrel
was interrupted by the arrival of a messenger who
brought the news that Clytemnestra and Iphigeneia, bringing with them Agamemnon's little
son, Orestes, had already reached the Greek
camp. The soldiers, who did not know yet for
what reason the royal ladies had been summoned,
imagined at once that they must have come for a
wedding and were thronging around the chariot
with shouts of joy and of congratulation.

Menelaus himself was moved when he listened
to the messenger's account of how this beautiful
and noble girl had come thinking that she was
about to be married, when in reality she was

being carried to her death. Though he, more than anyone, longed to be on the way to Troy, he had a generous heart and, forgetting the angry words that he had just been speaking to his brother, he grasped him by the hand and promised to do all he could to help him in saving Iphigeneia from the dreadful fate ordained for her by the prophet Calchas and the goddess Artemis. 'Let the army go home,' he said, 'and let us forget all our thoughts of glory and of vengeance! I would rather leave Helen where she is in Troy and find myself another wife than win her back at the cost of the life of your innocent daughter and your broken heart.'

Agamemnon was grateful to his brother for the generous affection which he showed. Yet now his own mind was overcome by cowardice. He feared that when Calchas and Odysseus told the army of the will of Artemis, the army would certainly demand that the sacrifice should be carried out. His daughter was now already in their camp and, if he should refuse to sacrifice her, the army would, he thought, turn upon him. Instead of being the commander-in-chief he would become a fugitive; nor would he in any case be able to save his daughter from her fate. It seemed to him that there was nothing now to be done except to perform the commands of Artemis. But, though he was chiefly frightened of the army, he was also frightened of his wife Clytemnestra, and he asked Menelaus to let her know nothing of the truth until the sacrifice had been made and the dreadful deed, for good or evil, was over and finished.

And now, in the middle of their words, Clytemnestra and Iphigeneia arrived. They had brought with them Agamemnon's little son, Orestes, a boy who was still an infant, too young to understand the happiness that had been promised to his sister and the very different fate which was, in fact, to overtake her. Iphigeneia herself, beautiful and affectionate, threw herself into her father's arms, weeping in her joy at seeing him again, and Agamemnon, as he felt the warm embrace and looked into the innocent eyes of his favourite child, wept too and turned his head away so that she should not see his tears. But she was quick to notice his mood and begged him to be cheerful, asking him whether she had done anything to offend him and whether she could do anything to relieve the anxiety which seemed to weigh upon him. Agamemnon, in his misery, told her that indeed she had done nothing to offend him; she was always the delight of his eyes, and what weighed upon him was the responsibility and cares of a general in the field; moreover he had an important sacrifice to attend to before the day was over.

'Can I take part in the sacrifice,' Iphigeneia asked, 'and lead the dances round the altar, as I used to do at home?'

To this question Agamemnon could not bear to make a reply. He kissed his daughter and again he wept tears. 'These tears', he said, 'are because of the long farewell that I must soon take of you. And now go inside the tent and rest. I myself must make the preparations for the sacrifice.'

So Iphigeneia withdrew and, as she went, she smiled kindly upon the father who was planning to take her life.

And now Clytemnestra began to question her husband about the arrangements that had been made for the wedding and about the birth and the qualities of Achilles whom she fancied was to become her son-in-law. Agamemnon gave evasive replies to her questions. What he wanted most was for her to leave the camp before the sacrifice took place, but, when he suggested that she should return home to Mycenae and leave the whole matter of the wedding in his hands, she was, as might have been expected, both angry with him for making such a request and determined not to grant it. She had a right, she said, to be present at her own daughter's wedding, and nothing would make her forego that right. Once again, then, Agamemnon found his plans miscarrying. Yet, though he could not persuade his wife to leave the camp, he was determined to conceal the truth from her for as long as possible.

Even in this, however, he was disappointed. For now he went away in order to consult with Calchas how the army should be told of what Artemis had demanded and of how the sacrifice should be performed. While he was away Achilles himself came to his tent. He was finding that his own troops, the famous Myrmidons, were becoming restive because of the delay in sailing and he had come to consult with Agamemnon as to the best means of keeping the men quiet.

The camp of Achilles was some way from that of Agamemnon and so he knew nothing of the arrival of Clytemnestra and of Iphigeneia. He was surprised when Clytemnestra welcomed him outside her husband's tent, and he was still more surprised when she addressed him affectionately as one who was about to become her son-in-law. 'I have never wooed your daughter,' he said to her, 'nor have I ever till this moment heard any mention of a marriage.'

At these words Clytemnestra was filled with shame and astonishment. It appeared plainly that some trick had been played on both Achilles and herself, but neither of them could imagine what could be the purpose of so cruel a deception. They were soon to find out the truth, for the old servant to whom Agamemnon had entrusted the letter that was never delivered, now that he found Clytemnestra alone with Achilles, came forward and revealed to them the terrible message of Calchas and the terrible danger in which Iphigeneia stood. It was for death, he told them, and not for marriage that Iphigeneia had been summoned from her home, and now he begged Achilles, whose name had been used in vain, to protect the girl who, in her innocence, imagined that she was betrothed to him. For this old servant was above all loyal to Clytemnestra and her family, since he had been in her service before ever she married Agamemnon.

Clytemnestra, horrified and distraught by the dreadful story she had heard, also implored Achilles to help her, if he could. As for Achilles, whose chief thoughts were always of war and of honour, he was furious that his name had been used when he himself had never been consulted. He was as eager as anyone for the fleet to be able to sail, and, had he been told that Agamemnon's daughter must die for the whole of Greece, it is probable that he would have agreed to the sacrifice. What vexed him most was that he had not been told. He had been rated below Menelaus and below Odysseus, whereas he regarded himself as being second to none in the army. Thus he was enraged against Agamemnon and swore that he would defend Iphigeneia in his own person and would, if need be, die for her rather than let the others so much as touch the hem of her robe.

Clytemnestra was grateful to him for the help he offered, but she saw clearly that, against the will of all the Greeks, not even Achilles could prevail. She told him that she herself would make one last appeal to her husband not to do this terrible thing and she urged him, when the assembly of the Greeks was held at which the words of Calchas would be made known to the army, to oppose the wicked resolution with all his force and all his influence. This Achilles promised to do and he promised also that, should he fail in this, he would still be willing to fight to the death in order to preserve Iphigeneia's life.

So Achilles went away to consult with his own troops and it was not long before Agamemnon returned to find his wife in a very different frame of mind from that in which he had left her. Most bitterly she reproached him with his treachery to her, his cruelty to their daughter and his cowardice in face of the army. And, as she saw that her complaints and her tears were having no effect, she brought forward Iphigeneia herself in front of her father and asked him, in her presence, how he could contemplate becoming the murderer of such a daughter. Iphigeneia joined her tears with those of her mother. She could scarcely believe it to be possible that a father whom she loved so dearly and who, she thought, loved her too, could consent to be her executioner. She loved the light of day and shrank from the darkness of death which threatened her. She had expected a joyful marriage and had looked forward in the future to welcoming her father in her own home and to seeing his pride in the grandchildren she would bear. But now, young and unmarried, with no dances and no happy songs, she was to be led, like some animal, to the altar of sacrifice.

Now indeed Agamemnon wished that he had never consented to the cruel demand of Calchas; but now it seemed to him that the decision was irrevocable and that nothing could alter it. He knew that at this very moment the Greeks were

CLYTEMNESTRA AND IPHIGENEIA BEFORE AGAMEMNON

meeting in an assembly and that Calchas was telling them what the will of the goddess was; he knew that they would be told that, unless Iphigeneia was sacrificed, Troy would never fall, nor would the expedition ever sail from Aulis; and he knew that such was the temper of the army that, however much they might pity the fate of an innocent girl, they would not let her life stand in the way of their great ambitions and their desire for war. And so, though he did not hide the grief he felt, he remained inflexible to the prayers of his daughter and of his wife. Partly to calm his own conscience he began to minimise his own responsibility for what was to take place and, as he left the two women and went away to hear what was happening at the assembly, he said to Iphigeneia 'It is not I and it is not Menelaus who wish this thing to be. It is not Calchas or Odysseus. No, it is something more important than any of us. Your blood is to be shed for the freedom and the greatness of Greece herself.'

These words, whether sincerely spoken or not, had their effect upon the noble nature of the girl, and, even in her tears, she began to recover her courage and to reflect that the death she shrank from was a death which would bring her undying honour. For on her alone depended the success and safety of the army and navy of the Greeks. The great warriors, each one of them, were prepared if need be to die in battle. Should not she, though only a young woman, also be ready to lay down her life for the good and greatness of her country?

Soon, indeed, came the time for her to do so. For now Achilles came hurrying to the tent straight from the assembly of the army. He had no good news to tell. The words of Calchas had been received with joy and with relief; in the whole host there was one overmastering desire, which was to man the ships as soon as the promised winds blew and to be upon the sea on the way to Troy. Only Achilles himself had ventured to stand up and to oppose the sacrifice, and, so furious had the army been at his opposition, that in spite of his great name and his brilliant qualities, even his own troops had threatened to stone him to death unless he ceased to interfere in what the whole expedition was resolved to do. Even now troops were on the way to escort Iphigeneia to the place of sacrifice. Achilles himself had come, as he had promised, fully armed and ready to die in her defence. Not that he had any hope of saving her, but he was determined not to break his word.

But now Iphigeneia gently declined to accept the help that he offered. 'Why should so many,' she said, 'be prepared to risk their lives for their country and I alone cling to my poor life, when my death is able to do such good? It is better to do the will of the gods without complaint and to help my fellow countrymen in whatever way I can do so. Indeed I am proud to die, since ever afterwards men will honour me for my death.'

As Achilles looked at the girl and saw the beauty and the resolution in her face, he wondered at her. Now he wished that the lying message of Agamemnon had been true and that this noble creature could become his wife instead of being led to the slaughter for the good of the army. And Iphigeneia, as she looked upon Achilles in all the beauty and strength of his youth, might herself have been glad to find such a husband; but now her mind was set on something very different from a wedding and, though Achilles still urged her to allow him to stand in front of her and shield her from the approaching guards, she would have none of his help. So Achilles departed, since it was his duty to be present at the sacrifice.

And now Iphigeneia said farewell to her mother, begging her not to be angry with her husband Agamemnon and to welcome him with love when he returned victorious from Troy. But Clytemnestra's heart was bitter within her: she would never forgive her husband for the part which he had played. Now, however, she could think of nothing but her daughter and she clung to her despairingly as she saw the guards approach who were to take her to be sacrificed.

Iphigeneia's own purpose never wavered. She freed herself from her mother's embrace. No violence was required to bring her to the appointed place. Instead she walked between the guards like a princess in some triumphal procession, calm and noble, holding her head high, and it seemed to her, as she went, that she was filled with some divine power and strength which was leading her on in a direction different from anything that she had imagined, towards something new and strange and glorious.

So she came to the place of sacrifice where all the army was assembled, and, as the men looked at her, they felt a holy awe and a deep compassion for her fate. Then the herald proclaimed silence; they crowned the maiden's head with garlands, and Calchas, the priest, took from the altar the keen knife which he was to plunge into her throat. But first, in the name of all the Greeks, Achilles prayed. 'O lady Artemis,' he said, 'accept this sacrifice that we offer, the innocent blood of a pure maiden; and grant to us in return favourable winds and that with our long spears we may overthrow the proud towers of Troy.'

And now the moment for the sacrifice had come. No hand was laid upon Iphigeneia and she unflinchingly bared her white neck to receive the blow of the knife which Calchas held. Meanwhile the leaders of the Greeks and indeed most men in the army stood with bowed heads, for, though they had approved the sacrifice themselves, they could not bear to see it carried out. And so Calchas raised the knife and struck and, as he struck, a great sigh went up from the whole army like the sound of a sudden wind through dry grasses. Yet in an instant the sighing changed to cries and exclamations of astonishment. For a miracle had taken place. At the very instant when Calchas had thrust the knife firmly at the girl's throat, the noble girl herself had changed or been dissolved into the air. Now, in the place where she had been, they saw a great stag gasping out its life upon the ground as the streams of blood issued from a great cut in its neck.

The army cried aloud in joy, for it was plain to all that the goddess Artemis herself had refused the human sacrifice and had, in her divine power, given the great stag to take the place of the noble daughter of Agamemnon. Iphigeneia herself had been carried away by the goddess, far from the haunts of men, to be her servant and companion. The greatness and generosity of her soul had been rewarded.

And now the winds began to blow from the shore. In joy and gladness the Greeks trooped down to the sea and began to man their ships. At long last the great expedition was to sail upon its way. Among the shouts of seamen and the clash of arms, Agamemnon said good-bye to his wife and told her that their daughter, so far from meeting death, had found honour with the blessed gods. But Clytemnestra's heart remained unchanged within her.

AGAMEMNON

AGAMEMNON

WHILE King Agamemnon was leading the Greek forces in their long war against Troy, his wife, Clytemnestra, was betraying him at home. She, during his absence, ruled in the rocky citadel of golden Mycenae and she ruled without check or hindrance, since all the great warriors had gone to Troy and only the women, the children and the old men were left behind.

Years passed and from the battle front, far away across the sea, news came infrequently and when it came it was bad news. The fighting seemed to have no end; more and more of those young men who had set out confidently to win glory and riches in the great war were reported as dead or missing somewhere in the plains of Troy, and those whose hearts ached for them, – fathers, sisters and wives – had nothing to console them, unless it were the dust and ashes of the dead sent home in a funeral urn. It was no wonder that, as the long time went by, there were some who cursed Agamemnon and his interminable war in which was perishing so much of the youth and strength of Greece; yet on the whole the people remained loyal to their King, praying for victory and for his return.

But these were never the prayers of Clytemnestra. If she had received the news of her husband's death, she would have laughed for joy at the hearing of it; for she hated her husband and she loved her husband's most bitter enemy. She had, or thought she had, good reason to hate Agamemnon; for, at the time when the great expedition was ready to set sail for Troy but was delayed by contrary winds, Agamemnon had listened to the words of the priests and prophets in his army and had been ready to sacrifice to the goddess Artemis his own daughter, Iphigeneia, so as to secure fair sailing weather for the fleet. It was after this that there had come to Mycenae one who, if Agamemnon had been there, would never have dared to set his foot across the frontier. This was Aegisthus, a man who was in no way the equal of Agamemnon, but who won the affection of Agamemnon's wife. Their guilty love was as a link in the chain of evil − evil which had been done before and evil which was to follow after. For Aegisthus' father, Thyestes, was the brother of Atreus, who was the father of the Kings Agamemnon and Menelaus. After the birth of these two princes Thyestes had secretly become the lover of Atreus' wife and by her had had children. In the end Atreus had discovered the shameful fact and he had taken a terrible vengeance upon his brother. He had invited Thyestes to a feast and had set before him to eat the flesh of his own children. Not till Thyestes had eaten of this flesh did Atreus reveal what he had done, and then

Thyestes, with a great cry, had overturned the table with his foot and had, though guilty himself, called down a great curse on the house of Atreus. He had then left Mycenae for ever, but, before he died, he became the father of Aegisthus, who was to do evil himself and to bring evil upon others.

Now, while all the best of the Greeks were fighting before Troy, Aegisthus came to Mycenae and was the lover of Agamemnon's wife. He and Clytemnestra did not live openly together in the splendid palace that stood on the height of the great fortress that looks out over the mountains and the wide plains of Argos to the sea. For they feared the people who, though many of them might grumble at the long war, still were loyal to their King and would never, so long as Agamemnon was alive, accept as their master one who, like a jackal, was sleeping in the bed where the lion had lain. Yet the love between Clytemnestra and Aegisthus did not go unnoticed. The old men, loyal counsellors of Agamemnon and of his father before him, longed for the day when the King would return and would set his house in order; but there were others who began to rest their hopes upon Clytemnestra and upon Aegisthus, as the war dragged on and on and as the King, with all the flower of Greece, still tarried overseas.

Suddenly came the news for which all had so long been waiting. One night the watchman on the roof of Clytemnestra's palace saw in the northern sky, outshining the gleam of star-light, the distant blaze of fire. As the flames grew and mounted he knew their meaning. He was watching the light of a beacon which carried the message that Troy had fallen. From mountain top to mountain top, from island to island, across the seas, the rivers and the plains this signal of fire had come from Asia into Europe, from the conquered walls of Troy to the citadel of Mycenae. As the watchman gazed upon the distant light he cried aloud in joy because he knew that the long war was over and that his master would return. But, knowing how matters were in Mycenae itself, he prayed to the gods that the Greeks, in their hour of victory, might be restrained from outrageous conduct and impiety and might return home safely and with the blessing of heaven. Then he gave the news to his mistress, and Clytemnestra, though no news could have pleased her less than that of her husband's return, had still to pretend that she was glad of it. She gave orders for sacrifices of thanksgiving to be made at all the altars of the gods; she joined in the singing and the dancing; she joined too in the prayers, though secretly her own were different from those of the others who longed to welcome back their dear ones; for already she and Aegisthus were making their own plans.

Meanwhile at Troy the Greeks had done just what the old watchman had prayed that they would be prevented from doing. After the long ten years of hardship, of wounds and of dangers, they had, in the moment of victory, lost all control over themselves. Old and young had been butchered in the streets of Troy without thought or mercy; oaths had been broken and the temples of the gods had been profaned. Thus the gods were angry with the Greeks and made their home-coming more difficult than their setting out. Many of them were to wander for years, driven by storms over the face of the ocean, before ever they were to return; others were to find in their own homes not peace and quiet but peril and even death.

Agamemnon was not one of those who had to wander for long over the sea before he reached his home. It was not many days after the message of fire had been received that he and his ships sailed into the harbour of Nauplia in the bay below the palace and fortress of Mycenae. Messengers soon brought to Clytemnestra the news of his coming. He came rich with the spoils of war and proud in his victory, but the men who accompanied him were few indeed compared with the number who, ten years previously, had set out on the great expedition; so great had been the slaughter beneath the walls of Troy. Among the slaves taken from the captured city Agamemnon was bringing with him Cassandra, the beautiful daughter of King Priam of Troy, to be his own handmaid. This princess, who was now a slave and chattel, had been in every way unfortunate. For the god Apollo himself had loved her and had given to her the gift of knowing the future; but then, either from fear or from modesty, she had rejected the god, and Apollo, though he could not take back the gift he had given, made this gift worthless. For he brought it about that, while Cassandra knew the future and could reveal it to others, no one would believe what she said. Thus she had known that Troy would fall and that she and her sisters and her old mother would be made slaves; she had urged King Priam and her brother Hector to make peace with the Greeks while peace could still be made and while still great Hector lived. But her true words were taken to be the idle ravings of a crazed woman. Now she went as a slave in the company of Agamemnon and, as she landed on this foreign shore, her prophetic heart began to stir within her. She dreaded the mountains in front of her and she half seemed to see already, what was still out of sight, the great palace of Atreus and his sons, a home of blood, towards which they were going.

And so, while Agamemnon, with the remnants of his army, with his slaves and his booty, made his way up from the coast to the fortress which was the capital of his kingdom, in Mycenae Clytemnestra prepared to welcome him, and, as she saw in the distance the band of veterans from Troy winding its way up the rocky paths, she prayed to Zeus that her own deeply laid and treacherous plans might be successful. She knew that, if she were to act at all, she must act at once, before Agamemnon could re-establish his authority or discover the extent to which already she had betrayed him. Meanwhile Aegisthus and his bodyguard were waiting in hiding near by.

So at the gateway of the palace Clytemnestra met the great King who was her husband. She looked at him closely and saw that the ten long years of war had left their mark upon him. There was a majesty and a strength in his bearing as he stood there, looking steadily in her face, and she, with all her resolution, trembled at the thought that he might already have been told something of her conduct. She spoke hurriedly and, had he indeed been suspicious, he would have noticed in her words a kind of exaggeration which would have shown that they were not sincere. She told him that all the time that he had been away she had wept for him continually; day and night she had been in tears at the thought of the dangers that might be threatening him; and for herself there had been not a single moment of joy or pleasure until this glad moment of her husband's return. And now, she said, she felt as she saw him like the shipwrecked sailor who suddenly comes in sight of land; to her his coming was like the sweet light in the sky that follows the tempest, like a cool spring of water which refreshes the weary traveller.

As she spoke, Agamemnon remained standing in his chariot, looking now at her, now at the people assembled about her. He was seeing his home and his people for the first time in ten years. And now Clytemnestra ordered her slaves to spread on the ground a great purple carpet. 'Let not my lord, the King,' she said, 'set his conquering foot upon the ground. Instead let him tread on purple, and let Justice lead him to his home!'

So saying, she bowed before him and all her slaves and attendants also prostrated themselves. But Agamemnon looked at her coldly. It seemed to him that she had protested too much; moreover he was a soldier and a Greek; it was not to his taste to be welcomed with this extravagance of bowing and of purple carpets as though he were some barbarian monarch. 'Give me,' he said, 'only the honour that is due to a man, and keep such ceremonies as these for the service of the gods.'

But Clytemnestra continued to beg and plead with him to do what she wished and in the end Agamemnon, though he made no secret of his displeasure, allowed himself to be persuaded to set his foot upon the costly glowing colours of the royal carpet. First, however, he removed his sandals, for he wished to behave with humility and not to invite the jealousy of any god as he went into his home. He turned also to Cassandra and told his wife to look after her well. Clytemnestra glanced at the strange foreign girl who had come with Agamemnon from Troy. She saw how her eyes were staring wide in terror at the great walls and battlements of this palace to which she had been brought. For, though Clytemnestra did not know it, the prophetic spirit in Cassandra was stirring. She knew that she was in a place of blood.

As for Clytemnestra, she looked coldly at the poor slave who had been loved by Apollo and who was Priam's daughter, since it was her purpose to kill Cassandra also, when the time came.

Meanwhile great Agamemnon strode along the purple into his home and did not know that, in what seemed a moment of perfect triumph, he was in fact going like a sacrificial beast to his own slaughter. Clytemnestra watched him go and then prepared to follow him so that she might carry out her own evil and cruel plan. First, however, she spoke to Cassandra, telling her roughly to get down from the chariot in which she stood and to go indoors with the other slaves. But Cassandra still stared fixedly in front of her, seeming not to hear the Queen's words; and not even when Clytemnestra raised her voice in anger did the prophetess pay her any attention. So, since she did not wish yet to show openly the violence that she planned, Clytemnestra left her standing at the gate, while she herself followed Agamemnon into the palace.

And now the troops who had for so long and so faithfully guarded their King in the perils of war dispersed to their own homes, believing that they had brought their master back to a place of peace. There were left outside the palace only Cassandra and some of the old counsellors of Agamemnon who remained to discuss among themselves what they knew of the past and what they feared or hoped for the future. They could never have feared anything so dreadful as what was just about to take place; for who could have imagined that a wife, unaided and with her own hand, would destroy her own husband, the greatest King among the Greeks, in the moment of his home-coming? Only to Cassandra, with the god's gift of prophetic insight, the whole evil of the past, of the present, and of the future was visible and alive. As she stared at the gigantic walls of Agamemnon's palace it seemed to her that the walls were running with blood and that stains of blood were spreading over the floors. Though she had never heard the story of the cruel feast that Atreus had placed before his brother Thyestes, in her mind's eye she seemed to see the figures of children holding in their hands cooked portions of their own flesh. She cried out in horror and now the great power of the god of prophecy, Apollo himself, descended upon her and overmastered her. She spoke in a voice that was no longer her own voice; her head and her limbs were tossed like leaves in a wind; her breathing was heavy and laboured as she tried to tell what she still saw through a kind of mist – the evil that was being done or that was about to be done. And, as the old men questioned her, they were both astonished and alarmed by what she said; for she told them what the god showed to her, all the past history of the crimes that had been committed in that place; she told them of what they either knew or suspected, that Aegisthus, while the King was away, had stolen into the heart and into the bed of the King's wife; and she told them that even now, at this instant, a web or net of death was being spread for Agamemnon himself. And now gradually the prophetic frenzy began to leave her. Her voice and manner became quiet and calm; her eyes lost their fixed and fearful stare; she seemed like a princess, though pitiful in her slavery, as she went herself into the palace, knowing that she was going to her own death.

Once more she had spoken the truth and once more it was not believed. For, though the old counsellors to whom she had been speaking, were indeed frightened by her words, they still could not bring themselves to imagine that those words were strictly true. Yet so it was. Inside the palace Clytemnestra had prepared a bath for her husband, knowing that he would wish to refresh himself after his journey. She had also cunningly prepared a robe, a wicked and treacherous instrument of death which, like a strait jacket, locked the arms of anyone who wore it, making even the strongest man impotent to defend himself. And so, in the bathroom of his palace, fettered in this robe, Agamemnon was slaughtered like an ox in a stall, slaughtered by the hand of his own wife who struck at him, defenceless as he was, with a heavy axe. Twice Agamemnon cried aloud before he fell to the ground in the streams of his own blood; but there was no one to help him.

Next Clytemnestra gave orders for Cassandra to be put to death. She had been the property of Agamemnon, and nothing of Agamemnon's was to be left. And now, as had been arranged,

Aegisthus came with his band of armed men. He had taken no part in the murder himself, but he was ready to share in its fruits and to make himself King of Mycenae and of Argos, ruling there with Clytemnestra as his Queen. So suddenly had the dreadful deed been done that those who were still loyal to Agamemnon were left confused, weak and incapable. The few troops that had returned from Troy were scattered about the city; the old counsellors who had heard the prophecies of Cassandra and who, to confirm these prophecies, had heard Agamemnon himself cry aloud in his death agony, were overawed and helpless when they found themselves confronted by Clytemnestra, exultant in the murder that she had done, and by Aegisthus with his armed men.

So Clytemnestra and Aegisthus reigned, and it seemed that they reigned securely. Yet there was an old servant in the palace who loved his master and his master's family. Directly after the murder this servant had hurriedly taken away Agamemnon's young son, Orestes. He and the young boy had ridden fast through the mountain passes to the north and had made their escape from Aegisthus, who, with or without the will of Clytemnestra, would certainly have destroyed any male child of Agamemnon. So Orestes lived and the curse still lived on that had haunted and was still to haunt the House of Atreus.

ORESTES

ORESTES

After Clytemnestra had killed her husband Agamemnon, she ruled in golden Mycenae and her lover Aegisthus ruled with her. Into their hands passed all the wealth of Troy which Agamemnon had brought back home with him – the gold and the slaves and the rich garments – so that their court was more splendid than it had ever been. Yet no one who has an unquiet mind can live happily, and, in the midst of all this wealth and power, both Clytemnestra and Aegisthus were vexed by the knowledge of the evil that they had done and by the fear that one day this evil would be avenged. They were flattered by their servants and their courtiers, but they were neither loved nor respected; nor could their soldiers or the strong walls of their citadel protect them from haunting thoughts in the daytime or from dreams in the night.

As for Clytemnestra, she had tried to quiet her own conscience by the plea that Agamemnon had deserved to die because he had been willing to take away from her one of her own children, Iphigeneia, to be sacrificed for the good of the army and the fleet. Yet now, by killing her husband, she had lost her other children as well.

Her son Orestes, who had been a mere boy at the time of the murder, had been carried away into safety by an old servant of Agamemnon's. He was being brought up far away in northern Greece and little news of him ever reached Mycenae, though it was clear enough that he must be growing up in hatred of his mother for what she had done and that, at some time or other, he might attempt to regain the kingdom which was his by right. As for the other child, Electra, she was a little older than Orestes and she, even better than he, had been able to realise at the time the meaning of the dreadful crime of which her mother had been guilty. She had remained in the palace and had seen day after day the proud love-making of the woman who had murdered her father and of the man who had not dared to look her father in the face. No words of self-excuse that Clytemnestra could address to her daughter had any effect upon the girl's hard embittered heart; for Electra could think only of one great fact, that her father Agamemnon, leader of all the Greeks, had been treacherously murdered by his own wife at the moment of his homecoming. As for Aegisthus, she thought of him with horror and with hatred; for how, she wondered, could her mother have preferred to her own great husband a man who had the good looks of a woman, but, though his nature was savage enough, none of the courage of a man. And so Electra passed her days and nights in bitterness and humiliation, giving her mother no love and receiving none from her. She prayed only that Orestes would return and would avenge their father's death, though, as the years went by and for long periods of time she had no knowledge of whether Orestes were alive or dead, even this hope would sometimes fail her and she would seem to see no end to her own sufferings and to the triumph of those who had destroyed her father.

It was to be expected that, as Electra remained constantly faithful to her father's memory, she would become more and more hated by Clytemnestra and by Aegisthus. Moreover she was not only hated, but feared. For, if she were to marry a man who was suited to her by birth, she might bear children who would be princes and powerful and who would certainly be taught that they should avenge their grandfather's death. And so, when Electra reached the age at which she might be married and when offers for her hand came from great men among the Greeks, Aegisthus and Clytemnestra, though they had no wish to keep Electra with them at home, still refused such offers. Instead they forced her into a marriage which, they thought, would humiliate her still further and would also serve their own interests. They gave her as wife to a poor peasant who lived in a rough cottage in the fields some way away from the great palace of the sons of Atreus. Thus they hoped to get rid of Electra for ever, for no one in future would want to marry her and she herself, with fresh hardships and sufferings in addition to the sorrow she had already, would

I

soon wear out in poverty her miserable life and would cease to be a trouble and a reproach to those who ruled in her father's palace.

Yet things did not turn out as Aegisthus and Clytemnestra had planned. It was true that Electra's life was miserable, but the man to whom she had been given in marriage, though he was poor enough, had a heart and spirit much more noble than were those of the usurping King and Queen. He pitied Electra for herself and he revered her as the daughter of Agamemnon, whose faithful subject he had been in the past. So, though he was forced to keep her in his poor cottage, he kept her with him not as a wife, but as an honoured guest; for he hoped that one day the murder of Agamemnon would be avenged and, if ever that day came, he wanted Electra to be free to marry some great man among the Greeks, as she should do, since she was the daughter of a King. For this kindness and consideration of his Electra honoured the good man who was, though only in name, her husband. She was forced to share his life of poverty, but she tried to lighten it for him by her care for his comfort and her diligence in the household tasks. Her sorrows remained, – her grief for her father, her longing and anxiety for her brother's return – but in this poor cottage to which she had been condemned she found more real kindness and more solid worth than she had ever known in the great palace where her mother and Aegisthus ruled.

Now all this time Orestes was growing to manhood under the protection of King Strophius of Phocis, whose kingdom was in the mountains beyond the Isthmus of Corinth. He had been brought up with the King's son, Pylades, and the two young princes became inseparable companions, sharing in each other's thoughts and actions, and so faithful to each other's interests that they became to later ages an example of what friendship could be. Both young men were strong and brave, but, while Pylades lived as a prince in his father's kingdom, respected and loved by all, Orestes knew himself to be an exile, cut off from his rights and deprived of his father because of his mother's wickedness. He grew up, in spite of his beauty and strength, with bitter thoughts in his heart and, when he reached manhood, he went with Pylades to the great temple of Apollo at Delphi to consult the oracle of the god. Here, among the towering mountains where eagles circle outwards from the heights and where the air is clear and bright as crystal, the god through the mouth of his prophetess gave the young man no uncertain answer. Orestes was told that he must go back to Mycenae and must there avenge his father's death by killing Aegisthus and by killing his own mother. This was the clear command of Apollo himself and dreadful punishments would fall upon the young man if he failed to carry out the task that was set before him.

So Apollo revealed his will to Orestes, but he did not reveal everything. He did not say that there exist terrible avengers for a mother's blood, the savage Erinyes, and that, by obeying the commands of one divine power, Orestes would be bringing upon himself the full wrath of another. As it was, everything seemed, in that high mountain air, clear and distinct. Though Orestes might shrink, as any son would shrink, from the thought of shedding his mother's blood, he knew his mother's crime, he respected his father's memory and he was supported by the certain authority and definite command of Apollo.

He set out therefore for Mycenae, determined to carry out the dreadful and dangerous enterprise, and his friend Pylades went with him, ready to share his perils and, if necessary, to die with him in the daring attempt. For it was a daring thing indeed for two young men to challenge the force and power of the rulers of Mycenae. They knew of no friends or allies in that country; all that was certain was that if it were once discovered who they were, they would instantly be put to death. However, they put their trust in the guidance of Apollo and set out for the land from which Orestes had fled so many years ago, when he was only a little boy. At that time even his sister Electra had been so young that she would now scarcely remember even what her brother looked like then; no one else, certainly, would recognise him, unless indeed that old man, the faithful servant of Agamemnon, who had carried Orestes to safety after his father's murder, still lived.

When they drew near to Mycenae they travelled secretly and by night. Before dawn they came to the great fortifications behind which was the palace of the sons of Atreus and now, standing in his own country, the first act of Orestes was to do honour to his father's tomb. The tomb was outside the city walls and had lacked the reverence that was due to it. Sometimes Clytemnestra, when she had been vexed with terrible dreams, would send offerings to the spirit of the man whom she had murdered; though no sacrifice that she could make would quiet her own spirit. Sometimes Aegisthus, in his wicked pride, would insult the tomb, pelting it with stones and mocking at the great man who lay within it. The people feared his rage and even those who were still loyal to the memory of Agamemnon did not venture to show their loyalty openly and would only dare to bring any offering to his tomb under the cover of darkness. So Orestes found his father's monument neglected and overgrown with weeds.

Here he knelt on the ground and prayed to his father's spirit, renewing the oath that he had made to the god Apollo, that he would not shrink from taking full vengeance for the murder that had been done. Then he and Pylades sacrificed a black sheep (since black is the colour which is proper in animals offered to the dead); and Orestes cut from his own head a long lock of hair and left it on the tomb as a pledge of honour to his father.

Now the sun was rising and they turned in the direction of the huts and cottages of the peasants who lived scattered along the slopes of the valley and in the plain below. They wished to enquire first where they could find Electra; they would not reveal themselves to her at once, for they did not know in what state she might be found or whether they could depend on her to help them. And so, by chance or by the guidance of the god, they came first to the poor cottage where Electra herself lived. The good man who was assumed to be her husband had already left his home for the fields, and Electra herself was frightened when she came out to draw water from the well and found herself confronted by two strangers, tall young men, with spears in their hands and with something fierce and hungry in the expression of their faces. But they spoke to her kindly and, when they began to ask her 'where does Electra live?', her first hope was that they might be messengers from the north who could tell her whether her brother Orestes was still alive. Orestes at once pretended that this was what, in fact, they were, for he did not yet know enough of his sister to know whether he could count on her for help in the dreadful deeds that lay ahead. Also he was surprised and horrified to find that she, the daughter of a King, was living in so poor a dwelling, so destitute of all good things. He told her that he was indeed a messenger from her brother and that he had been sent to find out what was the state of affairs in the kingdom of Mycenae.

At the news that her brother was alive Electra

was full of joy, and now she told the strangers, not knowing that one of them was Orestes himself, the story of her own life, – how she had been driven out of her father's palace and forced to marry a poor peasant, how this good man had respected her and shown her more kindness than she had ever known from her mother, how she prayed and longed for the day when her brother Orestes would return and would put an end to the guilty loves and lives of Clytemnestra and Aegisthus.

Orestes, as he listened, felt in his own heart joy and pride and love for a sister who, like himself, had never forgotten the wrong that had been done to their father, Agamemnon. He pitied her for the sufferings which she had undergone and, as she told her story, he could scarcely keep back his tears. Pylades also was moved with pity and with love as he looked at this young girl, so beautiful in face and figure, so gracious in her bearing, who had known in her short life so little happiness and so much misery and humiliation.

And now, when they were in the middle of their talk and before Orestes had been able to decide whether or not to reveal himself to his sister, the good farmer who was in name her husband returned to his house and was, as Electra had been, surprised and frightened to see strangers standing in front of it. But no sooner did Electra tell him that these were messengers from Orestes than he hastened to offer them all the hospitality that he was able to provide. He urged them to enter his house and to share with him the little food and wine that he possessed. Orestes thankfully accepted the generous invitation, but Electra, who knew how very little there was within the house, was glad to see that there was now approaching them an old man, a shepherd, who was their friend and who had been her servant. He was indeed that faithful follower of Agamemnon who, on the terrible day of his master's murder, had rescued the young Orestes and taken him to safety beyond the mountains. Ever since then he had lived with his few sheep and goats in the country far away from the palace where he had looked after the children of his king. So he had escaped the notice of Aegisthus and Clytemnestra; but from time to time he would visit Electra and the poor farmer with whom she lived. He would give them a lamb or a goat or whatever else he could afford to relieve their poverty and he, like they, would pray for the safety and for the return of Orestes.

Now, when Electra saw him approaching she was glad, since she knew that he also would welcome the news that had been brought and also that with his aid she would be able to give these strangers something better to eat than the few crusts of bread which was all her house contained. She quickly told Orestes who this man was and Orestes looked at him with affection, since it was indeed to him that he owed his own life.

As for the old shepherd, he scarcely noticed the

strangers at first, so excited was he with the news he brought. He enquired only whether he could speak freely and, when he was told that he could do so, he said what he had come to say. That morning he had been to visit the tomb of Agamemnon and, when he came to it, he had been amazed to find that someone had been there before him, had made a rich sacrifice and had left behind him a lock of hair. Who could this be? According to the old man it could be none other than Orestes himself, and he had looked closely at the lock of hair and found it to be of exactly the same colour and texture as Electra's own hair.

To Electra it seemed that the old man was saying what he wished to be true rather than what was true in fact. 'How I long myself,' she said to him, 'for Orestes to be here, but alas! he is still far away. I have good reason to know this, since these strangers have come from him and are his messengers.'

Now the old man looked at Orestes and Pylades, but soon he gave all his attention to Orestes himself, scanning every feature of his face with his keen eyes, trying, it seemed, to trace something there which was known to him alone. And at last he cried out 'Here, Electra, is the man himself. Here is your brother whom you have awaited for so long. Here, grown to manhood, is the boy whom I took to safety beyond the mountains. I know him by his royal bearing and by the scar above his eye. He got it when you and he were children and he fell down when the two of you were chasing a pet fawn in the palace of your father.'

So brother and sister were united again, and great was the joy they had in each other. Great too was the joy of the old servant who had lived to see the prince whom he had saved return again to Mycenae, and of the good man who had sheltered Electra beneath his poor roof. Now they all met together like friends long lost, with tears and with laughter.

Yet now, as they all knew, was not yet the time for rejoicing. In front of Orestes stood the great task of vengeance, a dreadful deed in itself and one that must prove difficult to accomplish. So they began to lay their plans, and what seemed to them best was this:

It was known that on this day Aegisthus would leave his palace and go into the country where, in a plot of his own ground, he was to make a sacrifice to the nymphs. No one would be with him who could possibly recognise Orestes and it seemed that, if Orestes and Pylades, pretending to be strangers, were to attend the sacrifice, and if the gods helped and guided them, some chance might occur of cutting down the tyrant in a moment when he had no suspicion of danger threatening him. And as for Clytemnestra, she also might be drawn out of the shelter of her palace and her guards. In order to do this Electra proposed that a message should be sent to her mother to say that she had just borne a male child and that she needed her mother's help in the proper ceremonies of purification which take place after childbirth. Clytemnestra would, in all probability, consent to come, not because of any love for her daughter but in order to see that she had in fact borne a child to a poor farmer, – partly out of curiosity and partly to insult one who had never yielded to her in her spirit. And once Clytemnestra had entered the poor cottage to which she had condemned her daughter, she would find that she herself was condemned to die there.

So they proceeded to carry out their plan. Orestes and Pylades went to the fields and orchards where Aegisthus was holding his feast and making his sacrifice to the nymphs. Aegisthus himself noticed the two young men and asked them who they were and from what country they came. They told him that they were men of Thessaly, from the far north, who were on their way to sacrifice to Zeus in Olympia. Then Aegisthus invited them to his feast. 'You men of Thessaly,' he said, 'are known to be good at taming horses and at severing the joints of animals prepared for sacrifice. You must join us at the feast which we make this day.'

Then Orestes and Pylades went in with the others over the green grass to the place chosen for the sacrifice. First a calf was sacrificed and, after he had cut the beast's throat, Aegisthus said 'Come, my Thessalian guests; take the knives and the axes and let us see your skill in cutting up the body. So Orestes took an axe and Pylades took a knife. Quickly they flayed and dismembered the carcase and cleft it open so that Aegisthus could look inside it and see by inspecting the warm entrails what, by the rules of prophecy, might be his fortune. As he bent his head to look, he saw that the liver of the slaughtered animal was misshapen and he saw other signs, all of which portended evil. For a moment Aegisthus shrank back. 'What can this be?' he said. 'One thing I fear, and that is the son of Agamemnon. Yet he is nowhere near me.' And so he peered down again into the body of the animal, seeking to find some more propitious sign. Then Orestes raised the axe high and, with the full strength of his arms and shoulders, brought it down upon the neck of Aegisthus, severing the head from the trunk, slaughtering him there like an ox, and like great Agamemnon himself had been slaughtered.

At once there was a cry of anger and dismay from the assembled guests and from the bodyguard of Aegisthus. Orestes and Pylades grasped their weapons and stood still. Before any move could be made Orestes cried out 'I, who have killed the tyrant, am no stranger, as you supposed. I am your rightful King, Orestes, the son of Agamemnon.'

The old servant was there to prove the truth of what he said and soon, among all the soldiers and servants of King Aegisthus, the cries of anger and of violence changed to shouts of joy. They laid their spears down upon the ground and crowned the head of Orestes with garlands.

Thus the first part of his task was done, but the second remained. The body of Aegisthus was carried back to the cottage where Electra was waiting anxiously to hear what had been the success of the attempt of her brother and his friend. She rejoiced at the sight of it and at the full vengeance that had been taken on the man who had betrayed her father. But the time for words was short, for now over the plain could be seen approaching the proud chariot of Clytemnestra. The message sent to her from Electra had had its effect and the Queen, with slaves and attendants at her side, knowing nothing of her lover's death or of her son's return, was coming to visit the daughter whom she had rejected.

And now, as he saw the bright chariots in the distance and knew that his mother was in one of them, for the first time the heart of Orestes shrank within him. How could he kill the mother who had given him birth? How could Apollo be good or wise, if he gave him so terrible a task to do?

Electra saw her brother's distress and was quick to urge him on to the final act. By killing their mother, she said, they would be righteously avenging their father; and the commands of the god of Delphi were too clear to be disobeyed. So Orestes and Pylades went inside the house and waited there for the deed which they had to do.

It was not long before Clytemnestra was at the door where Electra stood to greet her. Except that they were both beautiful, mother and daughter were different indeed to look at; for Electra was

dressed in the mean black clothes of a poor
woman, while Clytemnestra wore rich soft garments, brilliantly dyed. These were part of the
spoils of Troy, and Trojan women slaves, won in
battle by Agamemnon, were at her side to help
her dismount from her chariot and to attend on
her. Yet with all the pride of her bearing,
Clytemnestra was secretly afraid of this daughter
who had always opposed her and always remained
faithful to the memory of her murdered father.
There was no pity or love in Clytemnestra's heart
even now when she saw the wretched dwelling
to which Electra had been banished and believed
that inside it was a child newly-born. She wished
only to see the child, to take her part in the ceremonies of purification and to depart again
quickly; and so, with few words and drawing her
clothes about her so as to avoid dirtying them on
the smoky walls of the cottage, she went inside
the door, as unsuspicious of what was to befall her
as Agamemnon himself had been of her own plots
on the day that he came back from Troy.

Now her fate came upon her quickly. As soon
as her eyes grew accustomed to the dim light
inside the hut she saw on the ground a dead body
with the head severed from the neck and she saw
that the head and body were those of Aegisthus.
She turned to flee, but was prevented by strong
arms and, as she looked in the faces of the two
young men who held her, she knew that the one
of them who held the sword was the man whom
she most feared, her own son, Orestes. She cried

out for mercy, but no mercy was given to her.
Orestes had steeled his heart and there, obeying
the commands of the god, he slew his mother to
avenge his father's death.

He had done as the god in Delphi had commanded, but obedience did not bring content.
Now he looked with fear and horror at the work
of his hands. Terrible shapes rose up before his
eyes, dreadful creatures who would not let him
rest or sleep and which followed him like hounds,
seeking satisfaction for his mother's blood. These
beings were the Erinyes, implacable divine powers,
and by them Orestes was haunted night and day,
driven mad by their unceasing persecution.
Neither his sister Electra nor his friend Pylades
could comfort him, nor could his heart find rest
in the thought that he had only done the bidding
of a god. Though he travelled far and wide, he
failed to shake off his pitiless pursuers. Not until,
after many wanderings, he reached Athens and
put himself under the protection of Athene herself did he know any hope or any respite from his
sufferings. In Athens was given the final judgment between Apollo, who had commanded Orestes to kill the murderers of his father, and the
savage Erinyes, who would never rest till they had
extracted the full price for a mother's blood.
Under the guidance and power of Athene these
dreadful goddesses now relaxed their claims and
ever afterwards were worshipped under a different
name – 'The Kindly Ones' – in the city of Athens.
Orestes, having done much and suffered much,

was freed from guilt and the long tale of evil after evil which had fallen upon the house of Atreus now ended. Orestes reigned in the palace of his father. His sister Electra was given in marriage to his faithful friend Pylades; nor did the new King forget to honour the good man who had sheltered her in her misfortunes or that old servant to whom he owed his own life.

THE RESCUE OF IPHIGENEIA

THE RESCUE OF
IPHIGENEIA

THIS is another story told of what happened to Orestes when he was haunted by the Erinyes; and this story concerns also his long-lost sister, Iphigeneia.

It is said that even after Orestes had come to Athens to be purified from the guilt of having killed his mother and after he had received the protection of the goddess Athene, there were still some of those pursuing furies, the Erinyes, who would not leave him in peace, but continued to haunt him, so that from time to time he was driven mad by their persecution. So he went once more to the temple of Apollo at Delphi and asked for help, and indeed for simple justice from the god, since all his sufferings had come to him only because he had obeyed the god's commands. Apollo replied to him through his oracle and told him that one more task remained for him to do; once this had been carried out, he would be freed from his guilt and from the dreadful visions that would drive him mad. He was to make a voyage into the far north, through those blue and clashing rocks past which Jason had once sailed in the Argo. Beyond these rocks opened out the Black

147

Sea and on the northern coasts of the sea was a land of barbarians, the land of Tauris, where there stood a temple to Apollo's sister, Artemis. But here, in this barbarous country, the goddess was worshipped with cruel rites and with human sacrifices. All Greeks who were caught on this coast were taken to the temple and slaughtered at the altar in front of an image of Artemis, a holy statue that had fallen from the skies. And now Apollo commanded Orestes to go to this savage and desolate land, to steal the statue from the temple and to bring it back to Athens.

To Orestes this seemed a task which, though not so dreadful, was at least as difficult and dangerous as had been the carrying out of vengeance upon Aegisthus and Clytemnestra; yet, unless he undertook the dangers and the difficulty, he knew that he was doomed to a whole lifetime of misery and shame. His faithful friend Pylades had just married Electra, the sister of Orestes, but he would not allow anything to prevent him from sharing in the perils which Orestes had to face and he was determined to go with him. So he left his newly-married wife and prepared for the long voyage northwards to Tauris.

What neither Orestes nor Pylades knew was that the priestess of Artemis in Tauris was none other than Orestes' sister, Iphigeneia. She, it will be remembered, had suffered a most cruel fate at the hands of the Greeks. When the great expedition had been about to set sail for Troy under the command of her father Agamemnon, she had been brought to the seaport of Aulis, where the army and fleet were delayed by contrary winds, and there, by the commands of the priests and with the consent of her own father, she had been offered up, like an animal, for sacrifice to Artemis in order that the fleet might have fine and lucky weather for its sailing. At the very last moment, when the knife of sacrifice was being plunged into her heart, she had vanished into thin air and in her place a great stag was seen on the altar, drenched in blood that might have been hers. As for Iphigeneia herself, no one knew what had become of her or whether she was alive or dead.

In fact the goddess Artemis had preserved her life, had taken her up by divine power from the sight of the army at Aulis and had set her down in the barbarian kingdom of the swift-footed King Thoas in distant Tauris. Here ever since that time Iphigeneia had remained as priestess of Artemis, a Greek living among barbarians. It was her duty to follow the savage custom of the place, and so, whenever any Greek was captured on shore or sailing along the coast, it was she who had to consecrate him for sacrifice. Not that she herself ever stained her hands with human blood; what she had to do was to sprinkle water over the heads of those who were to be slain, and after that they were taken by the guards inside the temple, where they were slaughtered and their bodies burnt by fire. Thus Iphigeneia, who had, when she was only a young girl, been so nearly sacrificed by the Greeks, now became the priestess under whose authority many Greeks were themselves sacrificed. But it was from necessity, not from any wish for vengeance, that she performed this cruel duty and lived in this savage place. All the time she thought with longing of her distant home in Argos and in golden Mycenae. Sometimes rumours reached her of the great war that was fought at Troy and in the end she heard the news that Troy had fallen. But she knew nothing of the fortunes of her own family, nothing of her mother's treachery or of her father's murder. Most of all she longed to see her brother Orestes, whom she could remember only as a very small boy. She could never have imagined that he was now close to the wild country where she lived, fleeing from the avenging spirits whom he had roused against himself by obeying the dreadful orders of Apollo.

Nevertheless, since she was a priestess and one whose mind could be inspired by divine knowledge, she did have warning of what was to come, in a dream; yet, so unlikely did the truth seem to her, that she failed to understand it. She dreamed that she was again in her own room in the palace of Mycenae and that, while she slept, there was an earthquake. In her dream she hurried out of the house and saw all the roof falling in; only one pillar, the central pillar, remained standing and from the head of this pillar there seemed to come streams of yellow hair, while the pillar itself spoke with a human voice. She herself then sprinkled the hair with drops of water, as she used always to do over the heads of those who were to be sacrificed to Artemis, and while she sprinkled the water she wept and she woke weeping. When she was awake she tried to think what the dream could mean, and she rightly saw that by the destruction of her father's house was meant the death of her father and of her mother; the one pillar that still stood must mean Orestes, since sons are the pillars of their father's houses, and Orestes was Agamemnon's only son. But she could not imagine that Orestes would ever come to Tauris or that, if he did so, she could ever consecrate him for sacrifice; and so she failed to understand the last part of her dream. She thought that it must mean simply that Orestes was dead, and so she mourned all the more bitterly, being quite ignorant that Orestes was now near at hand and that with him she might herself be either saved or destroyed.

For, in the very night when Iphigeneia had dreamed this dream, Orestes and Pylades, with a ship of fifty oars, had put in to a creek on this wild coast, not far from the place where the temple of Artemis stood. They left their ship at anchor in the water near the shore, so that, if necessary, the crew would be able to escape, and they themselves landed and made their way along the coast till they came to the high walls of the castle where King Thoas lived and the temple, set back from the sea, where, as they had been informed, all Greeks who were found in this country were put to death. Neither of them knew that at this moment, inside the temple, Orestes' sister was thinking of her brother as of one who was lost to her for ever, or that, if indeed they were discovered, it was this sister of his who would have the duty of preparing them as victims for the sacrifice.

One glance at the firmly bolted gates of the temple and at the guards patrolling the battlements of the castle was enough to show them that they would have to wait for nightfall if they hoped to make their way unnoticed into the holy place and steal the statue for which they had come. So they withdrew to a sheltered bay where they hoped to remain unseen for the hours of daylight. However it happened that the bay to which they went, though it looked a desolate enough place, was visited from time to time by the herdsmen of the district, who used to go there to wash their cattle in the salt water of the sea. Some of these herdsmen from the slopes of the hills that surrounded the bay observed the two young men sitting by the edge of the surf, polishing their weapons and talking together. At first, when they saw their long golden hair, their strong limbs and noble bearing, they thought that these must be gods; but there were others among the herdsmen who were not so reverent, or not so superstitious, and who maintained that the two men were shipwrecked Greeks who were hiding because they knew of the custom of the land.

Meanwhile the herds of cattle had begun to make their way down to the beach, and now there came upon Orestes one of those fits of sudden madness which still afflicted him. He seemed to see in front of him those terrible avenging goddesses, the Erinyes, who had pursued him ever since his mother's death. Some had snakes twined in their hair; some waved flaming brands of fire, and one of them carried in her arms the dead body of Clytemnestra. With a great cry Orestes sprang to his feet, shaking off the restraining hand of Pylades, who tried in vain to comfort him. Raising his sword high he rushed upon the cattle and began to cut them down, for in these harmless beasts he seemed to see the terrible shapes of his pursuers.

So the sea was stained red with the blood of the slaughtered animals, and now the herdsmen gathered together in a body, blowing on horns and trumpets to summon aid from all in the neighbourhood, and began to hurl stones at the two young men surrounded on the shore. Soon the fit of madness that had overcome Orestes ended and Orestes himself fell to the ground in a faint. Seeing him in this defenceless state, the herdsmen pressed on, doubling their volleys of stones; but Pylades stood firm, sheltering his friend's body with his own body and behind the screen of his thick cloak which he held over him like a shield. And before long Orestes came to himself. He looked up and saw the mass of men surrounding them. 'O Pylades,' he said, 'it seems that Apollo has sent us here to meet our deaths; but, if we must die, let us at least die with honour!'

Then, shouting out his battle cry, he bore down upon the great numbers of his enemies, and Pylades went with him. Neither the herdsmen, for all their numbers, nor the soldiers who had come out to join them dared to stand their ground. Instead they fell back and from a safe distance shot arrows and hurled stones at the two Greeks. So they wearied them out and in the end with their stones they knocked the weapons from their hands.

In this way Orestes and Pylades were overpowered and were brought to King Thoas. When the King had heard what the herdsmen had to say he told them to take the prisoners immediately to the temple and to the priestess so that they might be sacrificed at once. 'These men,' he said, 'are without doubt great warriors among the Greeks. In sacrificing such men our priestess must feel joy, since she is avenging herself for what the Greeks would have done to her.'

So Orestes and Pylades, with their hands bound, were brought into the presence of Iphigeneia, whose duty it was to sprinkle their heads with water and to say over them the proper prayers. Meanwhile within the temple the attendants were making ready bowls to receive their blood and a fire in which their bodies were to be burned. This was the moment in which, after so many years, Orestes again saw his sister and Iphigeneia her brother.

As she looked at the young men in all their strength and beauty her heart was stirred to pity them. She could imagine the grief which must be felt by a mother or a sister at losing such sons or brothers as these. She was bound, she knew, to take her part in the bloody sacrifice, yet she wished to delay it, at least for a short time, and she questioned the two strangers, asking them their names and where they had come from. But Orestes would not tell her his name. He had no wish that it should be known that he, the last of the great house of Atreus, had died miserably in a barbarian country. Yet, since her manner was so gentle to him, he did not refuse to speak altogether. He told her that he and Pylades, though not brothers, were bound together by their friendship more firmly than any brothers could be, and he told her also that he came from Argos and from Mycenae.

When she heard these words, the names of the great cities of Agamemnon where she had spent her childhood, Iphigeneia sighed and she began again to question him. He told her the whole terrible story of which she had never heard, – of how Agamemnon had returned in triumph from Troy and had been murdered by his own wife at the moment of his homecoming, and of how the murder had been avenged by Agamemnon's son. Iphigeneia listened with amazement and with horror. 'And where is Orestes now?' she asked. 'Is he alive or dead?'

'Just now,' was the reply, 'he is alive. But wherever he is, he is unfortunate.'

At the news that he was alive at all Iphigeneia

ORESTES AND PYLADES BEFORE IPHIGENEIA

was strangely moved. It seemed to her that the dream which she had had must have been a deceitful dream; for even now she could not see its true meaning. Above all now she longed to send a message to her brother to let him know that she was still alive. It might be that at some time he might find means to rescue her from her exile on this barbarous coast and bring her back to golden Mycenae; and, even if this were too much to be hoped for, at least it would do her heart good only to hold some communication with him. So she spoke again to Orestes and said: 'Stranger, you say that you come from the land of Argos and of Mycenae, and you look as if you came from some noble family. Now there is some-one in that land to whom I wish to send a letter. If you will swear to carry this letter for me, I will spare your life and let you go free. I cannot spare your friend's life too, for neither the King nor the people of this land would allow it. But one of you I may spare.'

'Then', said Orestes, 'it is my friend who must take the letter while I remain here to die. Love for me, and no other reason, brought him with me on this adventure. Indeed it would be shame-ful if I allowed him to suffer death and went away safe myself. And in any case his life is as dear to me as my own.'

As Iphigeneia looked at the young man she admired him. 'Even though you will not tell me your name,' she said, 'I feel sure that you must come from some noble family. I pray that my own brother, who is far away from me, may be one like you, loyal and true to his friends.'

So she went inside the temple to write the letter that was to be carried back to Argos. But now Pylades in his turn protested that he would not save his own life, while Orestes was left to die. They were comrades together, he said, and as comrades they should live or die together.

Orestes begged his friend to take the letter and to live. He urged him to go back and comfort his sister Electra and to take not only his own kingdom but the kingdom of Mycenae as well. 'For myself,' he said, 'life cannot in any way be happy, since I shall still be pursued by the avenging spirits of my mother's blood; but you, Pylades, can live a noble and a fortunate life. In being kind to my sister and in honouring my memory you can give me pleasure even in the tomb. It seems certain that Apollo has cheated me, but you have never deceived me. Your friendship has been always the best thing in life that I have known. Now in the name of this friendship I beg you to live. Tell them in Argos that I died bravely and that I was only destroyed because I obeyed the commandments of a god. I killed my mother and now I must die myself.'

'As for me,' said Pylades, 'I shall keep my love for you whether you are alive or dead. Yet still we are both alive. It may still be that the gods will not cheat us – that some mercy may be shown.'

So they talked until Iphigeneia, with the letter in her hands, came out again from the temple.

First she put the letter into Pylades' hands and then she asked him to swear an oath that he would deliver it safely if she saved his life by interceding for him with King Thoas so as to let him go free.

'But,' said Pylades, 'supposing that I were to be shipwrecked and the letter was washed from my hands by the waves of the sea. Then I could not keep my oath. It would be better for you to let me learn the words of the letter by heart; then, so long as my life is saved, the words will also be preserved.'

Iphigeneia agreed to this and she began to read to him the letter that she had written. 'My words,' she began 'are for Orestes, the son of Agamemnon, and they come to him from his sister Iphigeneia.'

When they heard this, both Orestes and Pylades stood dumbfounded. Indeed they could not believe their ears, for both of them thought that long before this time Iphigeneia had perished at the hands of the gods.

Iphigeneia herself did not notice their confusion. She continued to read aloud the words that she had written: 'I who was sacrificed, they say, at Aulis, am still alive, though I am dead to those who love me. The goddess Artemis saved my life and brought me to this savage place where all my youth has been spent. Now, my brother Orestes, I beg you to come here and rescue me, so that I may see once again my own country and my own people.'

When she had finished reading she handed the letter to Pylades and, as she turned her eyes upon him and upon Orestes, she was astonished to see the expression in their faces.

'What you would have me do', said Pylades, 'is done easily enough', and he took the letter from her hand and gave it to Orestes. 'Here', he said, 'is your own brother, Orestes himself.'

Orestes clasped her in his arms, but she shrank back from him, for she could not even yet believe that this young man, whom she had been on the point of consecrating for sacrifice, was indeed the brother whom she had longed to see. It was not long, however, before Orestes convinced her that this was the truth, and then, with happy tears, she flung herself into his arms. Now, in this moment of joy, it seemed possible to forget the long tale of the sufferings of Agamemnon's house, all the treachery and crime and bloodshed that had taken place since that distant day in Aulis when an innocent girl had been brought forward as an offering for the success of the expedition against Troy. Now, in the dark recesses of his own mind, Orestes no longer felt the uneasy presence of the pursuing Erinyes. He knew again the affection that he had known in his childhood before the days of his exile and before he had been commanded by the gods to do the dreadful deeds that he had done.

There was much indeed that brother and sister had to say to each other, but there was not the time nor the opportunity for much to be said.

Orestes told her the reason why he and Pylades
had come, how they had been instructed by
Apollo to seize the statue of Artemis and bring it
to Athens, and Iphigeneia, though she was herself the priestess of Artemis, could see no wrong
in the deed, for Artemis was Apollo's sister and,
once the statue was removed to Athens, it would
no longer be worshipped with the savage ceremonies of human sacrifice. The difficulty was in
how to escape with the statue and with their own
lives, for the temple was guarded by King Thoas'
soldiers and at any moment the King himself
might be expected to arrive in order to find out
whether the sacrifice had been duly carried out.
Meanwhile Orestes and Pylades were defenceless;
for, though Iphigeneia had freed their hands,
their weapons had been taken from them.

It was Iphigeneia herself who thought of a plan
by which to deceive the King and to secure their
escape. When, as she knew would happen, King
Thoas came to the temple, she told him that a
strange event had taken place – something which
would make it necessary for the sacrifice to be
postponed. She said that, when the two Greeks
had been brought into the presence of the goddess, the holy statue itself had miraculously moved,
turning away its head from them. Then, said
Iphigeneia, she had questioned the two strangers
and had discovered that they were men who had
been driven out of Greece because they had been
guilty of shedding a mother's blood. Thus they
were impure and the goddess would never accept

L

them as a sacrifice until they had been taken to the sea, washed in the sea water and been purified from guilt with the proper prayers. Only she, Iphigeneia, could perform this ceremony and, while she was doing it, all the inhabitants of the city must stay within the city walls, in case they too should be involved in the guilt which was being washed away from the two men. Only a few priests from the temple should attend on her to make sure that the prisoners should attempt no violent escape.

King Thoas listened to her with attention, since he believed that in matters that concerned religion she was much wiser than he. Iphigeneia then said that the holy statue itself had been polluted by the presence of these strangers and that it was necessary to take the statue also down to the sea so that it could be ceremonially cleansed from the stain. Here again King Thoas accepted her advice. He gave the orders that she had required him to give. He himself with all his troops remained within the city walls; the statue was brought out from the temple, and soon a small procession began to make its way down to the sea. Iphigeneia, as the priestess, carried the statue herself; Orestes and Pylades followed her and the temple attendants guarded them.

So they made their way along the shore until they had almost reached the place where the fifty-oared Greek ship lay at anchor, concealed behind a headland, and at this point Iphigeneia ordered the temple attendants to bind the hands of Orestes and Pylades and to wait there while she herself performed the proper rites over them. The attendants could not dispute the commands of the priestess of Artemis, nor did they see how two men, unarmed and fettered, could attempt to make an escape. So they remained behind while Iphigeneia, carrying the statue and followed by Orestes and Pylades, went on farther along the shore until they were out of sight.

Time passed and still the waiting attendants saw no sign of their priestess returning. At length they began to grow uneasy and decided to go after her to make sure that all was well. But no sooner had they gone round the next headland than they saw a sight to surprise them, – a Greek war-ship, with fifty men sitting at the oars. The anchor was being raised and the hawsers drawn aboard. In the stern of the boat stood the two strangers, no longer bound, and with them was the priestess of Artemis, holding the statue of the goddess in her arms.

With their wild barbarian cries the temple attendants rushed down towards the shore; but they had arrived too late and there were too few of them to be able to resist the crew of the Greek ship. Standing in the stern Orestes cried out to them: 'Tell your King that it was by the will of the gods that I came here. I am Orestes, son of Agamemnon, a brother to this Iphigeneia, whom I am bringing back to her own home. Apollo himself preserves us and it was Apollo who commanded me to take this image of yours to Athens, where it will no longer receive the sacrifice of men's blood, but will be worshipped as the gods ought to be worshipped.'

Then he shouted to the rowers and the rowers bent forward over their oars. Over the whitening foam the ship shot like an arrow from that savage shore, moving too fast for any pursuit. So Orestes brought back his sister to her own land and so he himself at last found peace after all that he had suffered.

HELEN

HELEN

IT is well known how Paris, the son of King Priam of Troy, was called upon, while he was watching his sheep on Mount Ida, to judge a competition of beauty between the three goddesses, Hera, Aphrodite and Athene. The goddesses, each anxious to be the winner in this contest, offered gifts to Paris. Hera offered power and Athene offered wisdom; but Aphrodite told him that, if only he would declare her to be the winner, she would give him Helen, the most beautiful woman in the world, to be his wife. It is known how Paris was persuaded to give to Aphrodite the prize for beauty and how, by doing so, he brought utter ruin upon the great city of Troy and death to many men, Trojans and Greeks alike. For he stole Helen from her own home and her own husband, Menelaus, the King of Sparta and the brother of the powerful King Agamemnon; and it was to win her back again that there sailed from Greece the great expedition which for ten years fought in the plains of Troy. There Hector lost his life, and Achilles and many other warriors until, in the end, Troy was taken and Menelaus regained his wife, a woman whose faithlessness had caused much blood to be shed.

This is the story of Helen as it is generally told. But there is another and a different story of her. According to this other story Helen was neither wicked nor faithless. She was the victim of jealousy among the gods and she most undeservedly suffered much before, in the end, she became happy as she ought always to have been. This second story is as follows:

Aphrodite wished certainly to keep her promise to reward Paris for having given her the prize for beauty. And Paris, when he sailed away from Sparta, carrying with him a lovely woman whom he called 'Helen', was convinced that he had had his reward. In fact, however, this was not so. For Hera, in her anger at his having preferred Aphrodite to herself, had cheated him out of his real prize. She had given orders to the god Hermes to take Helen away from Sparta and to hide her in a distant land. And to take the place of Helen she had created out of thin air a phantom whom Paris took with him to Troy, and it was for this phantom that the Greeks and Trojans fought for so many years. No one could tell the difference between the real Helen and the phantom. Paris all the time believed that it was Helen herself who was his wife. Menelaus too, when the war was over, believed that he was carrying back again in his ship the woman to whom he had once been married and who had left him. Yet all the Greeks and all the Trojans who had fallen in this great war had fallen for something which did not really exist, since all this time Helen herself had never been in Troy at all.

The real Helen had been taken up by Hermes in folds of air, carried far away from her home in Sparta, from her loved husband Menelaus and from her little daughter Hermione, and set down in Egypt, where she was entrusted to the care of the King of that land, Proteus, a man who, though not a Greek, was one who revered the gods and who would obey their commands. He had been told by Hermes to keep Helen safe in his kingdom until the time should come for her husband Menelaus to find her and to take her home again.

And so for year after year Helen lived in exile in the palace of King Proteus. She was kindly and courteously treated, yet all the time she longed for her home and for her husband who, with all the great warriors of the Greeks, was fighting beneath the walls of Troy in the mistaken belief that he was fighting, not for a phantom, but for his real wife.

King Proteus had married one of the nymphs of the sea and by her had had two children, both of whom grew up during the time that Helen was in Egypt. The son was called Theoclymenus. He was a brave warrior, though he had a rash and hasty temper. His sister was called Theonoe and to her the gods had given the power of knowing what was happening in any part of the world, however far away, and what also was destined to happen. Thus she was a great prophetess and spent her life in the pure service of the gods.

Now so long as Proteus was alive Helen lived peacefully in the King's palace, though unhappily enough, since she was separated from her husband and her friends and she knew that throughout the world the story of her was that she was a faithless wife who had brought on her people the horrors of a long war. It was difficult indeed to bear the thought of all the hatred that was so wrongly felt against her and she often wept when she reflected upon what the gods had done to her. She was the daughter of Zeus himself who, in the form of a swan, had visited her mother Leda. Her brothers were the twin Dioscuri, the children of heaven, Castor and Pollux, who were among the greatest heroes of the time. Her husband was a King. She herself had behaved well and worthily of her great position, and yet all her family must certainly think of her as a wicked and disgraceful creature. It was true that Hermes had told her that in the end, when the will of the gods had been accomplished, she would be reunited to her husband and would return to her home in Sparta. But in the meantime what might not happen? Men were dying for her sake every day and women were being worn out with sorrow for husbands, brothers and sons lost in the destructive war.

So for ten years in Egypt Helen lamented her fate. Yet she was at least well treated and her person was safe in the care of the good old King Proteus. But a time came when even this consolation was taken away from her. Proteus died

HELEN AND THE PHANTOM

and his young son Theoclymenus became King in his stead. Now everything was changed. So long as his father had been alive Theoclymenus had had to obey him. He had treated Helen with the respect that was her due and he had followed his father's hospitable way of welcoming all Greeks (there were not many of them) who came to Egypt from time to time and could tell the latest rumours, true or false, of the great war still raging in the plains of Troy. But now Theoclymenus cast off all restraint. He was determined to make Helen his wife, whether she liked it or not, and, lest there should be any hope of her ever seeing her husband again, he gave orders to his officers that all Greeks landing in Egypt should immediately be put to death.

It seemed to Helen that now there was no escape open to her in this life, no possible way of relief. She was resolved to remain faithful to her husband Menelaus and to refuse the marriage offered to her, or forced upon her, by the young King of Egypt. Yet she had no one to defend her and no means now even of meeting with those who might give her hope from the news that they might bring. She fled from her room into the open air in front of the great gateway and battlements of the palace. Here was the tomb of Proteus and at this tomb she sought refuge, since even Theoclymenus, she thought, would not dare to violate his father's tomb by dragging her away from it by force. Yet still it seemed to her that there was nothing in which she could rest her hope. She began to look forward to death and even to contemplate how best she could take her own life. She did not know that, at this very moment when she was most vexed with terrible thoughts, her deliverance and her happiness were at hand.

Nor did she know that by this time, after its long siege, Troy had fallen and the victorious Greeks were on their way home. When finally she received the news it came to her in such a way as to make her even more unhappy than before. For one day a Greek who had fought in the Trojan war landed in Egypt and, not knowing that all Greeks were hated by the King of Egypt, made his way to the tall palace by the banks of the Nile. This Greek was Teucer, the famous archer and the brother of the great Ajax, who had been one of the foremost of all the warriors at Troy. In the end Ajax had met with a cruel fate. He had quarrelled with the other leaders of the Greeks and then the gods had taken away his right mind and made him mad. When once more he came back to his senses he was so ashamed that he took his own life. Teucer, his brother, had sailed home sorrowfully and when he reached his home in the island of Salamis that lies, shaped like a bean, off the coast of Athens, his father, King Telamon, treated him most unjustly. He blamed him, quite without reason, for his brother's death, and since he had come home without the great Ajax, no welcome was given to him and he was, after so many years of fighting abroad, driven

out again into exile. Now, with a chosen company
of men, he was on his way towards the eastern sea
where he was to found a city, another Salamis, in
the island of Cyprus. His ship had entered Egyptian waters undetected and had avoided the great
storm in which, as we shall see, another of the
Greeks had almost perished. So Teucer came to
the palace of Theoclymenus, intending to ask for
help and for guidance on his way.

The first thing that he saw was Helen standing
by the tomb of Proteus, beautiful and distressed.
He turned upon her and cursed her; not that he
believed that she really was Helen, because he
had seen with his own eyes that other Helen who
was a phantom carried off from Troy by Menelaus. But he so hated the woman who had been
the cause of all his sufferings that even to be reminded of her by one who, he thought, so closely
resembled her, made him half-crazy with anger.
Helen spoke to him gently. 'Why do you blame
me,' she said, 'for what I have not done?' And
Teucer was moved by her words and by her
manner. 'Forgive me,' he said, 'for my sudden
anger. But I and all the Greeks have suffered
countless miseries because of a woman who looks
so exactly like you that I can scarcely believe my
own eyes.' Then, still not knowing that it was to
Helen herself that he was speaking he told her
what he knew. It was, for her, a sad story to hear.
Troy, he told her, had fallen after ten years of
fighting in which many of the best of the Greeks
had lost their lives. Menelaus had sacked the

city and had taken away with him the faithless
wife for whose sake the war had been fought.
But a great storm had scattered the ships. Menelaus had never reached home and it was believed
that he and all his ship's company had been lost
at sea. At this news Helen could scarcely prevent
herself from crying out, but she found courage to
ask more questions and, as Teucer answered them,
she became more wretched still. Her mother
Leda, so Teucer told her, had hanged herself because of the shame she felt at her daughter's
conduct. As for her brothers, the Dioscuri, there
were two stories and Teucer did not know which
one was true. Some said that they also had died
because of the disgrace which their sister had
brought upon them; but others said that, because
of their virtuous and great deeds, they had been
set in the heavens like shining stars and had
joined the company of the gods. It was, as will
be seen, the second of these stories which was
correct.

Miserable as she was when she heard these
words of Teucer, Helen was still able to control
herself. She could not tell him who she was; for
in the first place, he would never believe it; and,
even if he did believe it, he would not be able to
help her to return to Greece, for he himself was
an exile. So she simply warned him to escape
from Egypt as quickly as he could, since King
Theoclymenus would kill every Greek whom he
found in his kingdom. Teucer thanked her for her
advice. 'Indeed,' he said, 'though you have a face

like Helen's, your heart is very different from hers. I pray that Helen may be drowned in the deep sea, but for you I wish every happiness that can come to you.'

So he went on his way and left Helen more unhappy than she had ever been; for now it seemed that she had been betrayed by the gods and had nothing to live for at all. Till this moment she had still believed, or half believed, that somehow and some day her husband would return to her, but now, if what Teucer told her was true, Menelaus was dead and had died without ever knowing that she had always been faithful to him. It seemed that she was wholly lost. She could marry Theoclymenus and be a queen; but that she was resolved not to do. It would be better, she thought, to die, and she began to plan how she could take her own life. Indeed her fate was a sad one. To other women beauty had always brought happiness, or at least the opportunity for it, but in Helen's case, it was just this great beauty of hers that had ruined her life.

One thing she determined to do before she killed herself. Theoclymenus, she knew, was out hunting. So she would leave the sanctuary of Proteus' tomb, go into the palace and there consult the King's sister, Theonoe, the prophetess who knew everything, both the present and the future. She was good and, if she were earnestly besought, she would tell her whether Menelaus was still alive or whether he had been lost in the waves of the sea. Helen dreaded to ask the question, yet ask it she must; for she could not kill herself unless she was certain beyond all doubt that no hope, not even the faintest, remained to her.

And so, walking carefully, in case she might be seized upon by some guard set for her by Theoclymenus, she left the monument which was her refuge and she entered the great gates of the palace, knowing that, once she had made her way to Theonoe, she would be safe, since the prophetess was so holy that not even the King, her brother, would dare to disturb one who had placed herself under her protection.

But no sooner had she gone inside the palace than the very thing for which she had so long been waiting actually took place. Menelaus, her husband, returned. But he returned in a way that was unexpected and no one who saw him as he drew near the palace would have guessed that he was a great King. For he came in rags, with hair and beard unkempt. His face bore all the marks of suffering and privation, for he had long been driven by storms across the angry seas as he tried to make his way back from Troy, carrying with him in his ship that phantom woman whom he had seized from the captured city and whom he believed to be his real wife. And now, by the will of the gods, his ship had been wrecked on the rocks just by the very place where Helen herself had so long been waiting for him. Menelaus had escaped from the wreck and so had most of his

M

crew together with that beautiful living image which they all believed to be Helen. It seemed to them that their case was desperate. They had lost their ship and were not even certain of what land they stood on. Menelaus had ordered his men to remain in hiding in a cave on the shore of the sea and there to guard his wife – for so he called the creature who had caused all his sufferings. He himself, seeing a great palace towering above the level plain, had determined to go there and, though a King, to beg for bread for himself and his company, and, if the people in this part of the world should prove hospitable, to ask for help as well.

So, just as Helen had gone inside the palace, terrified that she might be told by the prophetess that her husband was dead, Menelaus himself arrived at the palace gates, alive and strong, although instead of king's clothing he was dressed in wretched rags and instead of meeting with the reception due to a king he was forced to knock at the gate like any beggar.

As he knocked a woman servant half-opened the door, but refused to let him in. Seeing his miserable clothing she was at first for driving him away like a dog, but there was something in his bearing which impressed her and in the end she spoke to him kindly. When she discovered that he was a Greek, she warned him to escape at once. 'In our house,' she said, 'no Greek is welcome', and when Menelaus asked her the reason for this, she replied 'It is because the daughter of Zeus, Helen, is living in this land.'

Menelaus was astonished at the words. His wife, – the one whom he had just left in the cave, – could not have stolen away from there and reached the palace before him. 'What Helen do you mean?' he enquired and the woman answered him calmly 'Helen of Sparta, who came here before the Greeks set sail for Troy.'

Then she shut the door in his face and left him entirely bewildered. For how could he possibly believe what she said? He had fought in Troy for ten years and in the end had won back from that city a woman who to him and to everyone else was 'Helen'. He had just left her in the cave. Yet what was he to make of this maid servant's words? It occurred to him that perhaps in Egypt also there was a place called 'Sparta' and in this Egyptian Sparta there had lived a woman called 'Helen'. It sounded improbable; but what other explanation could there be?

And now, while he was reflecting on the strange words which he had heard and was wondering what next he could do to help himself and his companions, the gates of the palace opened and Helen herself came out from them. At first she did not notice Menelaus, for she was smiling to herself and her eyes were fixed in thought upon the ground. She smiled because she had heard good news. The prophetess Theonoe had told her the truth which was that, though her husband had been shipwrecked, he was alive and he was very close at hand. So, as she came slowly forward from the palace, she was occupied in pleasing thoughts. 'O when, when', she said to herself, 'will he come, the husband whom I have waited for so long?'

Then she raised her eyes and saw standing in front of her, between her and the tomb of Proteus which was her sanctuary, a tall strong man, wretchedly dressed and with every mark of hardship upon him. Her first thought was that this must be some servant of Theoclymenus sent there to intercept her and to prevent her from reaching the safety of the tomb. In terror she sprang past him and began to run the short distance that separated her from her place of sanctuary. Menelaus called out to her not to be afraid of him, since he meant no evil to her, but she would not stop until she had reached the altar which stood by the tomb. There she knew that she was safe and there, clinging to the altar, she turned to look more closely at the man from whom she had fled. Menelaus also looked at her and he was astonished at what he saw. 'Who are you?' he asked in amazement and now Helen, amazed too, since she saw beneath the wretched rags and all the marks of hardship the royal bearing which she knew, tremblingly replied 'I ask the same question. Who are you?'

'You look', said Menelaus, 'exactly as Helen looks.'

'And you', said Helen, 'look to me like Menelaus.' For, even though she knew him, she scarcely dared to believe in what she knew.

'Menelaus is indeed my name' he said. 'And it is the name of a man who has suffered much.'

At this Helen threw her arms about his neck. 'O welcome!' she cried, 'my husband! Welcome to your wife who has waited so long for you!'

But Menelaus unclasped her hands from his neck and stepped away from her. 'Wife!' he said. 'You are not my wife. I have a wife already, the woman whom I took from Troy. You look like my wife certainly, but the plain fact of the matter is that you are not.'

Then Helen tried to explain to him what had happened, that it was only a phantom who had gone to Troy with Paris and that she herself, his real wife, had remained faithful to him all these years in Egypt. Menelaus listened to her, but still he could not believe her. He thought that this was some trick or sorcery that was being practised upon him. For how could he and all those others have fought and suffered so long at Troy for something which was only a figure of air, something that was not the real thing? So, though he had now at last discovered his real wife and could have known her as a much better woman than he had thought, he could not believe in the fact, so much was his mind dominated by what he had thought previously and by the long years of his hardship. Indeed he would have left her there and then, in spite of everything she might have said to him and in spite of the perfect beauty which was her own, if it had not happened that he now received some strange news which made him, finally, acknowledge the happy truth.

Just as he had dragged himself away from Helen's arms there came running to the palace gates one of his own company, an old soldier who had fought with him throughout the war and who had been his faithful servant ever since the time long ago when he had married Helen in his own land of Sparta. The old man came in a state of great excitement and at first did not notice Helen while he hurried to tell his surprising story. What had happened was this: soon after Menelaus had left the cave the woman or phantom whom he and all the others believed to be Helen had risen to her feet with a strange look in her eyes and had briefly spoken to the men who gathered about her. 'Wretched Trojans', she had said, 'and wretched Greeks, all of you who died for me in battle and on the high seas, thinking that you were fighting for Helen, when you were only fighting for me, a creature made by the gods for their own purposes out of thin air! Now my mission is over and I must go back into the air from which I was formed. I tell you that you fought for nothing and that Helen, the wife of Menelaus, is innocent.' As she spoke these last words she melted away from their eyes into the surrounding air and the place where she had just been standing was left empty.

So the old man, bewildered and amazed, told his story to Menelaus. Then he noticed Helen herself standing in front of him and he became more puzzled than ever, since his first thought was that the woman who had so miraculously disappeared from the cave had now, in some equally miraculous way, reappeared in front of the palace. He did not know what to make of it. But Menelaus saw at once that this woman whom he had been on the point of rejecting was indeed his own wife, restored to him faithful and loving by the gods who had indeed treated both her and him cruelly but who had allowed finally the truth to be revealed. Joyful now indeed was their meeting, as they clasped each other in loving arms and each blessed the other for the happiness which they found together. As they began to speak and to tell each other of their fortunes, the old soldier, who had been bewildered at what he saw, began to understand what really had happened and he too rejoiced with them, for he remembered their marriage and, like a trusty servant, he honoured the good name of his master's house.

But now, after the joy of their recognition, the shadow of fear and of anxiety fell over them. For how were they to escape? Menelaus had lost his ship, so that the sea was closed to them. He and his men were brave warriors but they were too few to fight with the armies of the King of Egypt. Nor could they escape on land since Theocly-menus had chariots and horses which would overtake them. It was certain too that Theo-clymenus, who desired Helen for his own wife, would kill Menelaus, in spite of the fame and glory he had won at Troy, if he ever suspected who he was. Moreover it seemed impossible for him not to know, because Theonoe, his sister, could never be deceived and she, partly from fear and partly from love of her brother, would tell him that Menelaus, the man whom he most wished to destroy, was in his hands.

And so, as they entered into their difficulties and dangers, their newfound joy gave way to sorrow, for indeed there seemed no hope of their ever escaping from Egypt and its King. Menelaus could think of no plan except to take his stand upon the tomb and there die fighting; Helen would die with him rather than fall into the hands of Theoclymenus.

It seemed that what they feared would take place almost at once; for now Theonoe, the prophetess, with the priests and priestesses of her religion accompanying her, came out of the palace. She recognised Menelaus at once, for she was filled with divine power. The gods had been speaking to her and she knew that among the gods themselves there was argument and debate as to whether Menelaus and Helen should be allowed to live or not. Hera, the wife of Zeus, who had made the phantom in Helen's shape, now wanted to reward Menelaus for his sufferings by giving him back his true wife. But Aphrodite wanted them both to perish in case it should be known that she had not been able to keep her word to Paris and that he had enjoyed the love, not of Helen, but of a creature made out of the air. Now it was for Theonoe herself to decide

which of these goddesses should have her will.
For, if once she told her brother that Menelaus
was in his power, Menelaus, and Helen after him,
would certainly die. Loyalty to her brother and
fear for her own safety, if she should deceive him,
made her incline to tell him the truth. But she
listened to what Helen and Menelaus had to say
to her. They reminded her that her father
Proteus had been instructed to keep Helen safe
and, in due time, to return her to her husband,
and they begged her not to bring shame upon the
memory of her good father, who had acted
righteously all his life, by betraying the trust
which had been reposed in him. She herself, they
pointed out, was the servant of the gods and how
could it be right to serve the gods except by acting
righteously?

As Theonoe listened to them her mind altered.
She knew that it was wrong to betray innocent
people to death and she determined that she
would do right, even at the risk of her own life.
She promised them that she would not tell her
brother of the presence of Menelaus; but beyond
this she would not go. If they were to escape, they
must manage the manner of their escape themselves. She would not offend her brother further
by actively aiding them in the attempt.

And so she left them freed from one anxiety,
but surrounded with others. At any moment
King Theoclymenus might return from hunting
and, even if he did not know who Menelaus was,
he might put him to death simply because he was

a Greek. Once more it seemed that nothing was left to them except to die bravely, and death would indeed have been their fate, had not Helen, who was as intelligent as she was beautiful, thought of a clever plan by which to deceive the King and, if all went well, to secure their safety.

Her plan was to go into the palace and there cut her hair short and put on black robes of mourning, for she was going to pretend that she had received news that her husband Menelaus had been drowned at sea. Menelaus himself was to pretend to be the man who had brought this news; he was to say that he was a sailor on the ship that had been wrecked and that he had actually seen Menelaus die. Helen would then tell Theoclymenus that, now that her husband was dead and would never return, she was ready to marry him; but she would ask him first to let her have a ship so that she might sail out a little distance into the sea and there make the proper sacrifices and offerings for those who had been drowned and whose bodies would never be placed in a tomb. She would ask for rich gifts to be given to the dead and she would ask that Menelaus and his men (whom Theoclymenus would think were the survivors from her dead husband's ship) should join her in making the offerings. Then, once they were at sea, they would fight the Egyptian crew for the control of the ship and, if they were successful, would set sail for Greece.

It was a daring plan, but it was the only plan that seemed to offer any hope. Menelaus sent his

servant to tell his men to hold themselves ready
and to hide the swords they carried underneath
their garments, and Helen went into the palace
in order to dress herself as though she were in
mourning.

The plan had been made only just in time, for
now Theoclymenus rode up to the palace, surrounded by his attendants, his hunting dogs and
his horses. He was angry because he had been
told that a Greek had escaped the notice of the
guards whom he had posted along the coast and
had entered the land of Egypt. He was determined to have this man's life and would have been
more determined still if he had known that this
Greek was none other than great Menelaus himself.

Soon, however, when he saw Helen come out
of the palace, with her hair cut short and wearing
black robes, his anger gave way to astonishment.
She seemed no longer afraid of him but came
quickly towards him with bent head and told him
that she had now received certain news that her
husband had been lost at sea, so that now she
could accept the offer of marriage which Theoclymenus had made to her. At the same time she
beckoned Menelaus to come forward (for he had
hidden behind the tomb when he saw Theoclymenus approach). 'This is the man', she said 'who
has brought me the news of my husband. If it is
news that pleases you, I beg you to reward him
for it.'

Theoclymenus was conceited enough to sup-
pose that Helen really wanted to marry him. 'You

have done wisely', he said to her, 'and you shall have the most splendid wedding. All the nobles of Egypt will be present and will bring you gifts. You must not grieve at losing your husband. You will find me a much better man than Menelaus was. And as for this stranger' (and here he turned to Menelaus) 'since he has brought me such good news, his life shall be spared, he shall be given decent clothes to wear and I shall even invite him to my wedding banquet.'

Helen was pleased to find that Theoclymenus was so stupid and vain as to have fallen into the trap which she had laid for him. Next she asked him to show his love for her by granting her a request and Theoclymenus willingly agreed. 'There is a custom', said Helen, 'among the Greeks which is that, when a man is drowned at sea, his nearest relatives sail out in a ship and hold a funeral ceremony for him, even though his body is lost. I beg you to let me do this for my husband Menelaus.'

Theoclymenus at once agreed to let her have a ship for the performance of this ceremony. Being a barbarian, he was naturally impressed by Greek customs and asked Helen exactly what offerings were required for the dead. Helen replied that, for a man of the high rank of Menelaus, the ship should be loaded with clothing and armour and food of all kinds, together with animals for sacrificing. 'And then', she added, 'it would be a good thing if this stranger here (and she pointed to Menelaus) were to be put in command of the ship, since he and his men know the right way of making the sacrifices and how far exactly in the sea the ship ought to go.'

To this also Theoclymenus agreed. In a way he was pleased that Helen seemed so anxious to perform all the proper rites for her dead husband, for, in his vanity, he thought that she would have an equal respect for him as soon as she had married him. And so he gave orders to fit out a swift ship of Sidon and to provide all the gifts and offerings which Helen had asked for. Menelaus meanwhile was taken inside the palace where he was given a bath and presented with fine clothes. When he came out again, with all the marks of travel and of the shipwreck washed away, dressed as he ought to be and girt with his own sword, there was something so royal in his bearing that anyone less vain and opinionated than Theoclymenus would have marvelled at it and would have thought twice before handing over to such a man the woman whom he desired to be his wife. But Theoclymenus was so busy in making arrangements for holding his own wedding feast that it never occurred to him that there was any danger that this feast might never be held.

And now the rest of Menelaus's ship's company arrived, strong tough men, with fierce and eager eyes, veterans of the Trojan war. Each had his sword hidden under his garments and each was ready to fight grimly to win a way home again to the land they loved.

So Theoclymenus told the captain of his

Egyptian crew to obey the orders of the man he called 'the stranger' until the sacrifices were over and then to bring back to him the woman who was to be his bride. 'Do not mourn too much,' he said to Helen. 'Remember that you will soon have a husband who is a King.'

'That also is my prayer,' said Helen as she looked at Menelaus. Then Theoclymenus left them, and the animals and rich gifts were loaded on to the ship. The Egyptian rowers took their places at the oars; the sails were hoisted up; Helen and Menelaus went down the gangway and after them came the Greek sailors who sat together in the prow, waiting, tense and eager, with their faces fixed on Menelaus. Menelaus ordered the helmsman to steer the ship out to sea and, when they had gone some distance from the shore, he told his men to lift out of the hold the great bull which had been brought for sacrifice. Then he drew his sword and stood in front of the bull ready to cut its throat. The Egyptian rowers and officers waited, expecting that he would make some prayer for the dead man whom they believed that they were there to honour. But instead of this Menelaus lifted up his voice and cried out: 'O great Poseidon, god of the sea, grant my prayer. After all our sufferings, bring me and my wife home to Hellas and to Sparta.' Then he plunged the sword into the bull's throat and the blood spurted out directly into the sea, an omen which seemed to show that his prayer would be granted.

The Egyptians were dismayed. 'There is treachery on this ship,' they began to say. But Menelaus shouted out to his men: 'Now, my comrades, show these foreigners how you fought at Troy. Strike them down and hurl every one of them into the sea.' He himself sprang forward, dealing great blows with his sword, and his men followed him like wolves. As for the Egyptians they fought back with oars, with pieces of timber and with every weapon that came to hand, but they could not long resist these trained soldiers of the Greeks fighting to regain their native land. Only one of them escaped the slaughter and he, swimming in the sea, was picked up by another ship and taken back to land where he told King Theoclymenus that his bride had been stolen away from him and that 'the stranger' who had outwitted them was great Menelaus himself.

The anger of Theoclymenus was unbounded and it turned at once against his sister Theonoe who had known that Menelaus was present in the land and who had concealed her knowledge. In spite of all that his counsellors could do or say, Theoclymenus determined immediately to put his sister to death; but, as he was actually on his way to do this evil thing, he was prevented by the gods. For there suddenly appeared in front of him two shining figures like stars, strong and beautiful young men riding upon white horses. These were the Dioscuri, the brothers of Helen, who had not died but had been taken up into the heavens to join the gods. Theoclymenus was abashed by their presence and he listened humbly to their words. They told him that what had happened was the will of Zeus. It was right that Helen should be reunited with her husband, and Theonoe had done rightly in reverencing the commands that had been given to Proteus. Theoclymenus therefore must lay aside his anger and look elsewhere for a wife.

As he listened to the divine beings Theoclymenus felt the passion in his heart decline. He was glad that he had been prevented from committing a crime and he blessed Helen. 'For', he said, 'she is altogether exceptional among women, being not only beautiful, but also wise and faithful.'

As for Helen and Menelaus, fair winds carried them on their way over the green and the blue of the sea. After so many years of pain they were happy and happily they lived in Sparta. Nor did they ever know death, for when their years on this earth were over, the gods carried them to the Islands of the Blessed, a place where no keen winds come, no snow or storms of rain; gently the waves break on those sunlit shores and the mild air they breathe there keeps them young for ever in this garden that the gods have made for them. Here they know no sorrow and no toil, but live easily like the blessed gods themselves.